British Railway Signalling

by the same author

BRITISH STEAM LOCOMOTIVES AT WORK
CONTINENTAL MAIN LINES
STEAM LOCOMOTIVE

British Railway Signalling

A SURVEY OF FIFTY YEARS' PROGRESS

by

O. S. NOCK

B.Sc., C.Eng., F.I.C.E., F.I.Mech.E.,
M.I.Loco.E.
President 1969-70 session
The Institution of Railway Signal Engineers

London
GEORGE ALLEN AND UNWIN LTD

FIRST PUBLISHED IN 1969

© *George Allen & Unwin Ltd* 1969
SBN 04 625002 6

PRINTED IN GREAT BRITAIN
in 11 point Juliana type
BY THE BLACKFRIARS PRESS LTD
LEICESTER

Preface

The gradual evolution of British railway signalling methods from the traditional lower-quadrant semaphore, and heavy mechanical interlocking frames had only just begun when grouping of the railways took place, in 1923. There had been a good deal of pioneer work, and much discussion in the meetings of the Institution of Railway Signal Engineers; but opportunities to try out those early precepts had been few. A change was nevertheless coming over the scene, and from the early 1920s the development was striking in its principles, if not at first in its extent. It has continued with little or no intermission up to the present time. Far from there being any sign whatever of standardization in the control techniques associated with signalling practice, the development just now is more rapid than ever before.

It has been my life's work to be intimately associated with this great development, first as a trainee, then as a draughtsman, and finally holding the position of Chief Mechanical Engineer of the Signal Division of Westinghouse Brake and Signal Company during one of the most exciting and eventful times of the entire period under review, namely, when the British Railways Modernization Plan was launched in 1955. Then finance was suddenly made available to do resignalling work in this country on a scale never previously dreamed of, and I for one had the task of well-nigh quadrupling my own staff in a very short time in order to cope with the volume of design work that was involved. This is not, however, a book of personal reminiscence, though to be sure the forty-four years in which I have worked for Westinghouse contain many vivid memories of both men and events. It is primarily a book about signalling developments, and about the constant search for means of increasing safety, of increasing reliability, and at the same time contributing to the ever-present desire for faster and more frequent train services.

Inevitably there are personal memories that must obtrude into the story: recollections of men like Arthur Hurst of the North

Eastern, R. G. Berry of the Lancashire and Yorkshire; W. S. Every of the Underground, and most memorable among those signal engineers of thirty years ago, A. E. Tattersall of the London and North Eastern Railway, whose visions of the future, faintly decried by many of his contemporaries, are now becoming commonplace practice. It is indeed a fascinating story; as fascinating in looking back to its earliest years as in watching modern practice unfolding and giving glimpses of future possibilities beyond anything that was foreseen even by the visionaries of thirty years ago. The story ends at a time when the British Railways seem to be on the threshold of even more phenomenal developments in control methods, and when the idea of working an entire railway extending over many thousands of track miles from a single control room is not any longer a vision of the distant future, nor yet a possibility soon to become practical, but one which within a remarkably short time may become a reality.

O. S. NOCK

Contents

Illustrations

CHAPTER I

The Art of Signalling

Every form of locomotion needs some form of signalling at some time, even the pedestrian, who has to be alerted on occasion by notices such as 'mind your head', or 'mind the step'. It is inexorably a question of speed and ability to stop. On railways those two over-riding factors were evident from the very day the Liverpool and Manchester Railway was opened, when that distinguished engineer of later years, Joseph Locke, was driving the *Rocket*. Locke was suddenly confronted with an obstruction. He saw it clearly enough, but even at the moderate speed at which he was driving the brakes were inadequate and that obstruction, none other than Mr William Huskisson, M.P., was run down and fatally injured. There was insufficient warning, and the result was a tragedy.

For any set of circumstances—speed, brake power, weight of the train, gradient and so on—there is a precise mathematical answer to the distance at which warning of an obstruction ahead must be given to a driver; but beyond the mathematical answer to a specific problem there lies the extraordinary variety of circumstances that surround the day-to-day running of trains, even on modern non-steam railways. Thus in deciding the mode of signalling for any particular line, whether it be steam, electric, or diesel-operated, one has to establish a philosophy towards the problem as a whole. A modern computer can work out any specific problem with unprecedented speed and accuracy; but man has got to set the computer its task, and it is in deciding what has got to be worked out that signalling remains, as it always has been, an art and a philosophy and not an exact science.

In the early days of railways, while high regard was always paid towards safety in operation, the fundamental principles of signalling were not established overnight. In fact more than fifty years passed between the opening of the Stockton and Darlington Railway and the passing of the Act of Parliament that made compulsory the use of the absolute-block system on all passenger lines, and the fitting of all passenger trains with continuous automatic brakes. That came in 1889.

The block system, or to give it the strictly correct designation 'absolute-block' system, is still the cornerstone of British railway signalling. It is simply that the line is divided into a number of sections, of lengths varying according to circumstances, and that only one train is allowed in any section at any given time. The principle is just the same whether the sections are two or three miles long in mechanically signalled territory, or regulated by colour-light signals on a 100 m.p.h. electric railway, or again where the signals are very closely spaced as on the tube lines of the London Underground.

That having been said, the second fundamental feature of railway signalling comes into the picture. One cannot say to the driver of an express train 'stop!' Even on the roads, where the general use of pneumatic tyres on a relatively rough surface permits of very rapid deceleration, in emergency some preliminary warning is needed; one can see signs such as 'traffic signal ahead', or, on the motorways, no less than one mile preliminary warning is given of diverging roads, followed by a second warning at a half mile. On the railways, with steel wheels on steel rails, the rate of deceleration is much less than with road vehicles, even in emergency. Over the years various suggestions have been made as to how more rapid rates of deceleration could be obtained, by the use of different materials. But one has got to remember that in a train passengers are relaxed to a very much greater extent than in a road vehicle. They are not prepared for sudden deceleration. Even with brake power as it is there is sometimes disorganization in a dining car at an emergency brake application, and the kind of deceleration which is possible in an emergency with a road vehicle would bring luggage from the racks and cause serious casualties within the train itself—as an alternative to an outright collision. Thus the rate of deceleration on a railway must, of necessity, be gradual and drivers must be given warning of the necessity to stop in plenty of time, to make that stop without causing any discomfort to

16

Electro-pneumatics at King Edward Bridge, Newcastle

HEY-DAY OF THE SEMAPHORE

York South: a mixture of upper and lower quadrants

3. Waverley East, North British Railway

MECHANICAL BOXES

4. Acton Town
The first power-frame on the District Railway, installed 1905

passengers. Consequently the warning signal itself has to be placed some distance before the point at which the train would be required to stop.

If one fundamental of the art of signalling is thus so closely linked with the brake power of the trains, the other overriding consideration in all signalling work is the principle of 'fail-safe'. This can be expressed simply enough: if any part of the equipment should fail, if an electrical circuit be interrupted by a broken wire or a faulty contact, or any other mishap should occur either to the equipment itself, or the system, the result should be to give a danger, or warning indication to the driver of a train. At the turn of the century this principle was by no means universally accepted outside Great Britain and Ireland, though it was generally in practice in the countries of the British Empire, and in many parts of the USA. But to appreciate how things differed on the continent of Europe, for example, one or two manifestations of the principle may be quoted.

The standard stop signals in mechanical days provide an interesting first example. The British signals of the lower-quadrant type were so designed that if the rod connection to the arm broke, the counter-balance weight on the spectacle would return the arm to the horizontal position. I should explain that although the action of the signalman in pulling the lever to lower the signal imparts a pull to the wire from the signal-box to the base of the signal-post, the connection from the base of the post to the arm is a rod because an upward push is required to lower the arm. That in itself was a safety feature. With the introduction of upper-quadrant signals the action is a pull throughout from the lever in the signal-box to the arm itself. A pull was needed to raise the arm into the 'clear' position. If a wire broke the arm would drop to the horizontal, or danger position. Both varieties of British semaphore signals incorporated the fail-safe principle. The standard French 'stop' signal on the other hand was a carré, or red and white chessboard signal. This chessboard was displayed to the driver for the danger position, but when the line was clear the board was pivoted round on a vertical axis and became edge-on, so that all the driver saw—if he could see anything at all—was the thin edge of the board. The French used to work on the principle that no signal at all was 'all clear'; but of course, if the carré was blown completely away, or fell to the ground one could have the same indication as that of a legitimate 'clear' signal, in other words nothing at all. Failure in the mechanism in a French stop signal could lead to a very dangerous state of affairs.

With the introduction of colour-light signalling, the fail-safe principle was incorporated in the circuits controlling such signals, and the equivalent of a broken mechanical connection, such as a broken wire or a bad electrical connection, was arranged to result in the danger indication being shown to the driver—all the intervening electrical appliances being designed on the fail-safe principle. But in colour-light signalling one came finally to the signal itself, and the question naturally arises as to what would happen if one of the lamp bulbs should burn out. In standard colour-light signalling what is termed 'lamp-proving' is incorporated; in other words, there is a definite electrical 'proof' that the lamp is actually alight. If a lamp should burn out the control circuit to the *preceding* signal is interrupted, and that signal would immediately show red. The guiding principle is that a train should be stopped before it comes to a colour-light signal on which a lamp has burnt out.

One factor that inevitably arouses a good deal of discussion among signal engineers is the aftermath of a failure. The apparatus, whether it be mechanical or electrical, if correctly designed will show the danger indication; and the next train to arrive, and succeeding ones behind it, will all be brought safely to a stop. What happens then? The failure may take some time to clear. It is imperative that traffic be got on the move again as quickly as possible, providing there is no definite obstruction to the line; but while the failure persists the signalman cannot clear the signals, and therefore some special instruction must be given to drivers. It is then sometimes that, under verbal instructions, orders are misinterpreted and mistakes made. Generally however the working under such emergency conditions is most closely supervised, and the regulations carried out with such deliberation and exactitude that in some cases of delay passengers are apt to get impatient, especially if they know little of what is going on. Many such cases of emergency may appear to proceed infuriatingly slowly; but it is far better to be slow and safe rather than attempt to hustle things, and possibly, through hastiness, cause the very accident which the fail-safe feature of the equipment has prevented.

In this connection I should like to tell a story of how instructions can be misinterpreted and a serious contretemps, if not necessarily a disaster, could arise. Some twenty years ago the signalling at a large terminal station in Great Britain was being changed from semaphore to colour-light, and the final stages of the change-over work were planned, as usual, to take place at a week-end. The major works were to be carried out during the Saturday night and early Sunday morning. It was a big job and the number of men working in the area concerned was considerable. The working instructions to the train crews stated that from a time around 11 p.m. on the Saturday night all signals in the neighbourhood of the terminus would be disconnected; drivers should ignore all signals and proceed with extreme care, looking out for hand signals and being prepared to stop with very little notice. The engineers had obtained possession and the change-over work was getting well into its stride around 11.30, when someone on the ground mentioned almost casually that the last express from 'X' had not yet arrived. He had hardly spoken when there was a noise of what was thought to be a very 'rough shunt'. As there was a large goods-yard nearby nobody for the moment thought anything more of it, until news came through some twenty minutes later as to what that 'rough shunt' was!

Apparently the driver of that last express had duly read his instructions, but then had interpreted them somewhat freely. He had started ignoring signals a good three miles out of the terminus, and the fact that he was diverted to an unusual route had not surprised him, because in the circumstances of the moment he appreciated unusual workings were in force. By his premature ignoring of signals he had actually been diverted on to an empty carriage line. Having ignored the signals at the point of diversion and continuing to run at a speed that was injudicious, to say the least of it, he received no more signals until he found himself entering a carriage shed. It was too late to do anything about it then, and he completed this unorthodox route by colliding head-on with another locomotive inside the carriage shed—fortunately at a low enough speed to avoid any serious damage and casualties. It was several hours, however, before that trainload of passengers was extracted from their temporary terminal point, and the train worked through properly into the station.

The art of signalling is inextricably bound up with the practice of railway operation, and the regulations for working in unusual circumstances have been gradually built up over the years with just as much care, and on a wealth of practical experience, as signalling for ordinary working. Apart from this one reference to 'regulations' as distinct from working to signal indication, I do not intend to go further. 'Rules and regulations' in railway working are a subject in themselves, and in this book I am concerned about signalling itself.

Until the turn of the century all signalling in Great Britain, except for one experimental installation at Granary Junction, Spitalfields, was mechanical, using lower-quadrant semaphore signals. Then developments in America, and to a lesser extent on the continent of Europe, brought about the beginnings of a change in the first decade of the twentieth century. The use of compressed air for actuating brakes and the increasing use of electricity as a servo-mechanism turned the thoughts of British railway engineers towards the lessening of the amount of manual work in signal-boxes, and in that same decade a number of installations were commissioned in this country in which either electricity or compressed air, or a combination of both, was used for the physical work of moving the semaphores, shifting the points, and moving the facing-point lock-bars.

At first electricity was used to a very limited extent for other than purely actuation purposes. Electric indicators and electric means of detection of various functions had but a very limited application, and track circuiting was in its infancy. It was the historic disaster on the Midland Railway at Hawes Junction on Christmas Eve 1910 that resulted in the first extensive application of track circuiting as a general safeguard in railway operation; but the onset of war in 1914 brought all such promising developments to a temporary halt, and the work done between the installation of the first British example of power signalling at Granary Junction, Spitalfields, in 1898 and the end of the war in 1918 can be regarded as no more than a curtain-raiser to the real development of power signalling that took place from about 1920 onwards. This is not to belittle in any way the work done in those early years; because it included the commissioning of some very large installations, such as those at Newcastle and Hull on the North Eastern Railway, and at Glasgow Central on the Caledonian. Furthermore the signalling equipment of the London Tube railways was, for its period, highly sophisticated, including track circuiting and the provision of automatic train stops adjacent to all the 'stop' signals. But signal engineers and operating men alike continued to think of the semaphore arm as the basic 'signal', and it was only a very few who were then foreseeing that there might be a time when something quite different might be substituted for 'signals' as they were universally accepted up to the year 1914.

It is surprising in the circumstances that the first hint of some exceedingly forward thinking in the art of signalling should have come from that most conservative of railways, the Great Western, and it came when the signal engineer of that railway, A. T. Blackall, delivered the inaugural presidential address to the newly-formed Institution of Railway Signal Engineers in 1912. In a very striking and prophetic passage he said:

'Now if the root idea involved in the expression "signalling" be the control of traffic movements, it is clear that the actual means adopted to effect that control, though essential features, are subsidiary ones. They will vary under varying conditions; they will vary from time to time; they may entail the use of mechanical appliances, of electrical or other power, or they may consist merely in the application of a code of rules. Thus, the primary and most essential function of signalling consists in the consideration, in a comprehensive fashion, of the whole of the conditions which have to be met, and the whole of the requirements which have to be fulfilled; and, having regard to all these, in the working out of a scheme which shall be appropriate from every possible point of view. It is thus obvious that to think of the signalling arts as concerned merely, for example, with the installation of semaphores, the connecting up of rail switches, or the equipment of block apparatus, is to take a very incomplete and one-sided view of its functions; it is to think, in fact, of one or more individual parts as representing the whole.

'Each of the many functions into which a signalling equipment may be divided is important, as assisting to the object which is in view, but it should never be forgotten that the need for any of them may be transient only. By a turn in the wheel of development any one of these may become useless, when to retain it would be merely to hinder progress. Now it is by cultivating this attitude of mind that the successful signal engineer is produced. He must have at his command all the many schemes and devices and systems and appliances which the experience of many years of development has provided for him; but all these he must regard merely as tools, to be made use of or discarded as the necessities of the moment may demand, in fulfilment of the essential purpose of the art of signalling as I have attempted to define it. Thus, for example, and the conception is not a remote one, if the conditions in a given case be met most satisfactorily by a signalling system in which there were no semaphore or other visible signals, and no block system, there should be no hesitation in adopting it, and the fact that the ancient features had been scrapped, and ancient methods discarded, would in no way remove such a scheme from within the definition of a signalling system.'

Fifty-six years later, in company with some fellow members of the Institution of Railway Signal Engineers, I travelled on the new Rotterdam Metro, which had been opened to the public only a fortnight earlier, and on which an intensive service of the fast electric trains is operated without any visible signals at the lineside. The intervening stages, in the years 1912 to 1968, form one of the most fascinating stories of railway engineering and operating evolution.

CHAPTER II

A Survey in 1922

The closing months of the pre-grouping era in Great Britain form a very convenient point at which to survey the state of the art of signalling, and to review the extent to which power methods had begun to replace the traditional mechanical working of points and signals. At that time, except for one or two isolated installations, the lower-quadrant semaphore signal was standard throughout the country. The detailed construction of the semaphores themselves differed very considerably as between one company and another, and connoisseurs have delighted in studying and modelling the semaphore signal configurations of the various companies. There was a world of difference, for example, between the ribbed-steel arms of the London and North Western Railway, made in the locomotive works at Crewe, and the plain wooden blades of many other railways—very often seen reinforced near the end with a thin steel band to prevent the blades splitting along their length. Then again, the method of mounting on the post varied from the simple pivot brackets used by many railways to those quaint survivals of the earliest days of semaphore signalling practice in which the arms worked in a slot in the main post. Arms of this latter type were standard on the North Eastern Railway, Southern Division, until after grouping had taken place. It was nevertheless remarkable that the Southern and Northern Divisions of this one railway had different standards, notably in the design of the semaphore arms and in the type of mechanical interlocking frame used. Such was the long-established tradition in the Southern Division of the North Eastern Railway of having arms working in a slot in the post, that, when lattice posts were introduced for the power signalling installed at Newcastle in 1906, the lattice posts, at considerable complication and expense, were also constructed so that the arms could be mounted centrally, as on the wooden posts.

So far as main-line running practice was concerned in 1922, the indications given to the driver were standard. The great majority of signals gave two indications: horizontal for 'stop', or 'caution' in the case of a distant signal; or inclined downwards for 'proceed'. Where one had a home and distant arm on the same post, three indications were given: both arms inclined down, 'proceed at full speed'; upper arm down and lower arm horizontal, 'proceed with caution'; both arms horizontal, 'stop'. The variations in signalling practice as between the numerous companies that existed prior to the grouping was to be seen in their methods of indicating shunt, calling-on, or other subsidiary movements. For these purposes all the individuality of the various railway companies came into full play, and an extraordinary variety of different signs and symbols were used to portray different meanings. Where one railway company had running powers over the tracks of another, as at stations like York and Carlisle, the trains of many companies entered one large station. Then it was not enough for the drivers to know the signalling practice of their own company; they had to know the peculiarities that existed at such joint stations. Entry into these joint stations was probably the only instance they experienced in all their workings of the particular types of shunt and subsidiary signals.

Immediately prior to the outbreak of World War I, many English engineers had been making a close study of what was happening in the United States of America. There the upper-quadrant type of semaphore signal was coming into favour, partly because with its use it was possible for a single semaphore arm to give three indications: horizontal for 'stop', inclined upwards for 'caution', and pointing vertically upwards for 'all-clear'. A small but influential body of British railway operating opinion was inclined to the view that some development and improvement of our traditional code of aspects was becoming desirable, in order to handle efficiently our ever-increasing railway traffic, and from certain experimental installations of isolated signals there came the interesting and extensive electrically-operated upper-quadrant signal installation on the South Eastern and Chatham side of Victoria Station in London. To some British engineers this installation was a symbol of progress; to others it was an undesirable 'Yankee' intrusion. To the arguments of one engineer who stressed the simplicity of the three-position signal in preference to the traditional British two-arm 'home' and 'distant' combination, a very celebrated British engineer said that he did not like it because it was like trying to tell the time from a one-handed clock. It was much easier to tell the time from a two-handed clock!

Nevertheless the upper-quadrant semaphore signal showed some signs of increasing in popularity immediately after World War I. An experimental unit of this kind had been installed on the down departure line at Paddington, Great Western Railway, for many years, and what could have been construed as the shape of things to come was next to be seen in the use of the same type of signal on the Ealing and Shepherds Bush Railway. This line, which was owned by the Great Western, ran from a terminus adjacent to the main-line station at Ealing Broadway by a circuitous route through North Acton to a junction with the Central London Railway at Wood Lane. It was electrified and used almost entirely by tube trains of the Central London Railway. In addition to this installation in London, the Metropolitan Railway had a number of electrically operated upper-quadrant semaphore signals, but these latter were all of the two-position type.

Quite apart from the question of signal aspects, as displayed to the drivers, a number of large and important installations of power-worked semaphore signals had been commissioned in various parts of the country prior to World War I. These were mostly conceived as labour-saving devices, enabling signalmen to control wider areas than previously because they were relieved almost entirely of manual work. The majority were installed on the electro-pneumatic system with compressed-air cylinders for operating points and applying power to lower the signals. The work on the ground was very largely indistinguishable from that seen in mechanical areas. Protection of the facing points, to obviate the risk of their being moved while a train was approaching or passing over, was effected by means of the traditional facing-point lock-bars, and communication with adjacent signal-boxes and sometimes between one power-box and another was made through the ordinary block instruments, just as would have been done had the boxes themselves contained interlocking frames of the manual type. Installations of this kind were made at Hull Paragon, North Eastern Railway, at Newcastle Central, North Eastern Railway, and at Glasgow Central Caledonian Railway, among many others. At the last two stations the installation of power signalling took place when general reconstruction of the stations themselves was carried out; at Glasgow when the Clyde Viaduct was widened and access to the station from the south side greatly improved; at Newcastle when the entire layout and working was altered following the opening of the King Edward Bridge over the Tyne in 1906.

The electro-pneumatic signalling at Newcastle provides a very good example of the application of power to the control of a large installation without any of the refinements of track circuiting, illuminated diagrams, and the combination of facing-point locks with the power-operated point mechanisms. In the new 'No. 1 box' there was a total of 283 levers to work 236 signals and 119 pairs of points. This may be compared with the equipment of the previous No. 1 box at Newcastle Central in the final mechanical days. At the turn of the century the mechanical 'Newcastle No. 1' was the largest locking frame, in one length, anywhere in the world and contained 244 levers. But the economy in size by the use of power can be appreciated from the fact that the pitch of the levers in the mechanical frame was 5 in. whereas that in the electro-pneumatic frame which replaced it was only 2¾ in. The new installation in the Newcastle No. 1 box formed no more than a part of the total electro-pneumatic signalling installations in the Newcastle area and there were, in addition to the No. 1 box, and the almost equally large No. 3 box at the west end of the central station, a number of smaller boxes on the south side of the River Tyne, controlling the various junctions which led to the southern approaches to the King Edward Bridge on the one hand, and the High Level Bridge on the other. All these signal-boxes, although equipped for full power operation of points and semaphore signals, were in communication with each other by means of the old-fashioned bell code, and the advantage from the use of power lay solely in the fact that the signal-boxes were more compact, and that the men, by being relieved of a great deal of the physical work of pulling levers, could concentrate more thoroughly upon their true functions—that of traffic controllers.

The installation on the Caledonian Railway at Glasgow Central

Station, as finally developed, became the largest single power inter-locking frame ever to be constructed as one unit. It had 374 levers, and controlled 253 signals and 112 pairs of points. To some extent its design was very soon out of date, because the number of levers in relation to the functions operated was large. The practice that developed very soon after this installation was put into commission would have enabled combination to have been made of many of the functions operated, so that the total number of levers could have been greatly reduced. Nevertheless this installation at Glasgow remained, throughout the fifty years of its existence, a milestone in the gradual evolution of British signalling practice. Without power signalling and a miniature locking frame of this kind it would have been quite impossible to have operated a station the size of Glasgow Central from one control point.

Although it was quite old-fashioned, even by the standards of 1922, mention must be made of another installation of electro-pneumatic signalling which was in fact the very first put into service anywhere in the British Isles. This was the relatively small plant at the entrance to Bishopsgate Goods Station, Great Eastern Railway, the box at Granary Junction, brought into service in 1898. The signals and points were worked by compressed-air motors, and, as at Newcastle and at Glasgow, power was used purely for the elimination of manual work. The interlocking frame was a direct import from America and was of the standard Union Switch and Signal Company's type which the Americans used then to call a 'table interlocker'. It is not so much the form of the interlocking machine, however, that makes the plant interesting from the viewpoint of the present theme, but the method of indicating the lie of the points. At the rear of the machine on a vertical board there was a diagram of the tracks, and on this track diagram the actual lie of the points was shown by mechanically moving a small flag indicator, in synchronization with the movement of the corresponding point levers. Thus a signalman not only had lever handles to indicate the state of the yard at any time, but he could see, on this animated mechanical diagram, the actual lie of each pair of points. So far as I know this was the only British installation in which this feature was incorporated, though it was common enough in the USA at that time. The introduction of track circuiting made the illuminated track diagram possible, and provided a much simpler means of indicating the actual routes that were set in any particular layout.

Another very interesting feature of power signalling introduced in the first decade of the present century was the Sykes electro-mechanical system. Two of the most important installations of this kind were at Victoria, London Brighton and South Coast Railway, and at Glasgow St Enoch, Glasgow and South Western Railway. This system was in some ways a half-way house between full mechanical and full power working. The points were operated by full-size levers through mechanical rodding, and the signals were controlled electrically by miniature slides. The point levers were grouped together as in an ordinary mechanical frame, and the signal slides were contained in a row about the level of the block-shelf in a conventional mechanical box. There was mechanical interlocking between the signal slides and the full-sized point levers. By designing the control instruments in this way their overall length was roughly halved, as compared with a full mechanical frame. The signalmen therefore did not have to walk up and down to the same extent, and they were relieved of all the heavy work of pulling signal levers. One thus obtained a notable degree of compactness, and by retaining mechanical operation for the points, the installation was much cheaper to instal than a full power plant. At both Glasgow St Enoch and Victoria, a number of the signals were electrically operated semaphores; but in both places a large number of signals were of the Sykes illuminated-banner type, which were found very suitable for installing under station awnings and in other places where space was limited and the sighting of conventional semaphore signals could have been difficult.

Another form of power working, with all-electric operation, was that known as the 'Crewe' system. It was developed on the London and North Western Railway, and provided for the electric operation of points and semaphore signals. A miniature lever frame was used, and with concentration of control of large areas in a limited space such, for example, as the north and south junctions at Crewe itself, a very great length of locking frame would have resulted if it had been arranged in a single row, as in the case of the signal-boxes at Newcastle and Glasgow Central mentioned earlier in this chapter. To secure compactness the locking frame was arranged to have two tiers of levers, the upper tier lying a little to the rear of the lower one and thus halving the length of the locking frame. A number of installations of this kind were put into service on the London and North Western Railway at Crewe itself, at Manchester London Road, and in the approaches to Euston. A similar apparatus was built by The Railway Signal Company and installed at Severus Junction, York, North Eastern Railway, controlling the entrance to the main line from the very large goods sorting sidings lying to the north of the city.

Another system which was used extensively, particularly on the London and South Western Railway, was the low-pressure pneumatic, which in contrast to the electro-pneumatic system used air pressure at no more than 15 lb. per sq. in. against the 50 or 60 lb. per sq. in. used for the electro-pneumatic. The low-pressure pneumatic was a closed-circuit system, thus requiring two pipes to every function that was operated. The movement of the lever in the interlocking frame operated air valves and set the system in motion, while the completion of the circuit and the return flow of air was used to act as a proving device indicating that the function had actually responded. The design of the locking frame was so arranged that the signalman could pull a lever to no more than three-quarters of its full stroke. The completion of the stroke was made by the return air after it had completed the circuit and actuated the necessary valves, energized the points or cylinder motors as the case might be. With the electric or electro-pneumatic system the lever is pulled over to what is known as the check-lock position, and when detection is forthcoming that the function has correctly replied an electric lock is released to enable the lever stroke to be completed. In the low-pressure pneumatic system the completion of the lever stroke was done automatically, and the term 'dynamic indication' was used to describe it. Interlocking frames were of the slide type as distinct from the conventional form of miniature lever. One distinguishing feature of the low-pressure system was the large size of the point cylinders. This, of course, was necessary due to the low pressure used, in comparison with the high pressure of the electro-pneumatic system.

One of the most interesting, and perhaps the most familiar installation of the low-pressure pneumatic was that controlling the automatic signals on the London and South Western main line

29

between Woking and Basingstoke. On this quadrupled-tracked section many gantries with four doll-posts spanned the tracks, and each of these dolls had a home and distant arm. They normally stood in the 'clear' position with both arms off. After the passage of a train the arms would go to danger, and subsequently first the home and then the distant arm would clear according to the occupancy of the line ahead. It was actually three-position automatic signalling, using a two-arm instead of a single-arm signal. The engineer responsible for this installation, A. H. Johnson, was the man who averred jocularly that it was easier to read the time with a two-handed, rather than a one-handed clock, and he certainly followed out this dictum with the automatic signalling between Woking and Basingstoke. These automatic signals actually remained in service for nearly sixty years. They were not dispensed with until multi-aspect colour-light signalling was installed in 1966 in connection with the electrification of the Bournemouth line.

Generally speaking, all these British systems of power working had as their basis the traditional practice developed under manual block, of separate levers being used to operate points and signals. Before signals could be lowered to permit a train to follow a certain route, the signalman had to go through the process of setting all the individual points, and only when these were set and the detection had proved that the switch blades were truly against their respective stock rails was the interlocking freed to enable the signal lever to be pulled. With power working, certain combinations of control made it possible to reduce the total number of levers in a locking frame. In certain cases 'push-pull' levers were used which stood normally in the central position. The case of a simple junction would make this clear. There would be two semaphore arms, one reading for the main line, and one for the branch, and the push-pull principle could be used to the extent that the 'push' action would control the main-line signal and the 'pull' action the branch, so that only one lever was needed to actuate two signals.

There was, nevertheless, a trend in the period around the end of World War I to reduce to a far greater extent the amount of lever pulling a signalman had to do by use of route working throughout: in other words, the ideal was aimed at of a man only having to pull one lever to set up an entire route. After the interlocking was free, the pulling of such a route lever would, from the one movement, set all the points in the positions required, and when the points were set, and correspondingly detected, the appropriate signal would clear. Practical details of such a system were worked out between Mr L. M. G. Ferreira and Mr R. J. Insell, the latter then Assistant Signal Engineer of the Great Western Railway. The system was first installed at Winchester Cheese Hill, on the Didcot, Newbury and Southampton line; and having been thoroughly tried out at this small and not very busy station, the Insell-Ferreira system was installed at Newport (Monmouth) on the South Wales main line of the Great Western. This form of route working, using miniature levers, was destined to be the only one of its kind; but although very heavily worked at Newport, it gave excellent service and lasted for nearly forty years.

In concluding this survey it is important to appreciate that in 1922 and for a considerable number of years afterwards some of the largest and busiest stations in Great Britain were operated entirely with mechanical signalling. On the Southern, for example, there were London Bridge, Cannon Street, and Waterloo; there was Euston, and one of the busiest of them all, Liverpool Street. Away from London were Birmingham New Street, York, Manchester Victoria, Carlisle, and Edinburgh Waverley. Later chapters of this book will describe how these stations were converted to power operation, but the ways in which they were managed in mechanical signalling days were outstanding examples of railway operation, in the perfect co-ordination that took place between the work in the signal-boxes, the work on the footplate, and the work on the station platforms. Standing on the ends of the platforms at Liverpool Street during the evening rush hours, it was hard to imagine that the smooth intense working was the result of a large team of men, everyone of whom knew his job to the nth degree. So smooth was the operation, and so quick, that it was hard to believe that every movement was not the product of the workings of some gigantic computer. At that time, of course, computers were unknown: but to see the comings and goings of the trains, the slickness with which points were operated after trains had passed; to see how quickly light engines backed on to the coaches in the platforms, and how quickly the clearing of signals was carried out, was to appreciate how optimum working could be obtained with mechanical signalling and entirely steam traction.

At London Bridge there was a small amount of electric train working on the Brighton side, and at Waterloo in the year 1922 the 'Riverside Electric' had got fully into its stride; but both London Bridge and Waterloo were then predominantly steam, with all the additional complications of light-engine working and empty stock movements. Euston had one of the largest mechanical frames to be found anywhere in the country, having 277 levers in the No. 2 box; but unlike some of the large mechanical frames elsewhere, the levers were not in one single row. The frame was in two halves with the signalmen in each half working back to back, and a certain amount of the locking necessarily below the floor on which the men worked. Waterloo was notable for a considerable amount of special lever arrangements and mechanical locking designed to minimize the number of levers required for working this vast layout; but the technical details of that installation belong to an earlier period than that with which I am now concerned.

The traffic at stations like York, Carlisle and Edinburgh Waverley was of a generally different character to that handled at London terminal stations like Waterloo and Liverpool Street. The amount of local traffic terminating at these stations was relatively small, and the many problems in working arose from the intense peaks of through traffic that took place at well-defined intervals during the day and night. In 1922 practically every train that passed through York from north to south changed engines, and at Carlisle engines were changed without exception, because through trains were passing from the English to the Scottish Companies. The arrangements for handling this business of engine changing were highly organized, and at Carlisle the traffic working arrangements were such that locomotives for the through Anglo-Scottish trains had to be received from or despatched to five different engine sheds, two north and three south of the main passenger station. The interested passenger, or railway enthusiast, could watch enthralled from the station platforms, and although there might be delays of a kind he could marvel that there was so little, and that even when pressure was at its greatest none of the men concerned seemed to lose their heads or their tempers. The secret was to be discovered when one had the privilege of going behind the scenes, as I have had on several occasions; and I can think of no better example of the kind of work that had to be done in one of these large through

Irwell Bridge, Lancashire and Yorkshire Railway

MECHANICAL BOXES

Victoria West, Manchester L. & Y.R.

7. Earls Court, with electro-pneumatic semaphores and L.N.W.R. 'Outer Circle' train—Mansion House to Broad Street

EARLY DAYS ON THE UNDERGROUND

8. Aldgate, looking towards Liverpool Street

Looking down the line, showing three successive signals

BRITAIN'S FIRST COLOUR-LIGHT SIGNALS—
LIVERPOOL OVERHEAD RAILWAY

A crowded train apparently waits for the photographer

11. The electro-mechanical locking frame

SYKES ELECTRO-MECHANICAL AT ST ENOCH

12. Bridge of signals at the platform end

stations in the days of mechanical signalling and steam traction than to take a glimpse behind the scenes at York on a summer Saturday morning in the very height of the holiday season.

In mechanical days the working at York was controlled by four signal-boxes having a total of 391 levers. These were distributed as follows, proceeding from south to north through the station: at the southern end there was Locomotive Yard box with 129 levers; in the centre of the station adjoining the main footbridge was the central box with seventy levers, and then at the north end there were two boxes. Of these, Leeman Road, with sixty levers, was concerned with the west side of the station and down main-line traffic. Waterworks cabin with 132 levers dealt with the up main-line traffic on the approach to the station, and with the Scarborough branch. Every train passing through York from south to north had to be handled by at least three out of these four boxes. Trains terminating at the south would be dealt with entirely by the Locomotive Yard box, while Waterworks would deal entirely with trains from the Scarborough line terminating at York. But take the case of a through East Coast express from King's Cross to Edinburgh, or farther north, which would be dealt with at the down main platform passing through the very centre of the station; it would approach from the south under the control of the Locomotive Yard box, and then its passage through the centre of the station would be controlled by the Central cabin. The down starting signals at the platform end were controlled by Waterworks, after which it would be handed over to Leeman Road in taking the down main line to the north.

Obviously the most perfect co-ordination was needed between these four signal-boxes in handling through traffic, and the co-ordination, as I saw it on several occasions, was provided in the most dynamic way by the Assistant Stationmaster of the shift. At York the Stationmaster himself had three assistants who turn and turn about handled the three eight-hour shifts throughout the twenty-four hours. The Assistant Stationmaster on duty was usually to be found in the Central cabin constantly telephoning, constantly talking with his finger on every single movement that was taking place in and around the station. He knew the traffic like the back of his hand. He realized in a second the complications that could arise from the late running of any particular train, and

C

he had working with him in the signal-boxes, on the platforms, and in the locomotive yards, men whose experience and efficiency was second only to his own. His was an art and a craft that no study-courses, no book-learning could teach. He was a lifelong railway-man, dedicated utterly to his task and backed up by senior signal-men, platform inspectors, and locomotive foremen who were no less devoted to their work. I have seen the great changes that have since come over railway operation, and was closely associated with the design work that made that change possible at York; but even watching the result of my own handiwork in operation in the great central control room, that now takes the place of the four boxes just mentioned and many more, I can still look back with a glow of enthusiasm for the men who used to work that station in mechanical days, when the actual traffic working was considerably more complicated than it is today.

One does not need to look back to the past through rose-tinted spectacles. There were times when there were some mighty hold-ups. When the working *did* get out of gear it was very difficult to untie the knots and restore punctual working, and I have the most vivid recollections of a journey from King's Cross to Edinburgh just before a Bank Holiday when we arrived in Edinburgh about one and a half hours late. Believe it or not, nearly all that lateness was spent in standing time, first outside York, then outside New-castle, and then outside Edinburgh itself. Each station had got thoroughly out of gear, and it is at such times that the modern control machine with its illuminated diagram shows up to immense advantage over the old methods. In mechanical days the work of men like the Assistant Stationmaster at York was geared con-stantly to avoid delay, and prevent congestion by anticipating it and stopping it before it began to pile up. That is where the life-long experience of a dedicated railwayman was worth more than much elaborate machinery.

Many of these great mechanical installations that were in exis-tence in 1922 continued in service for many years into the transi-tion period between the purely mechanical era and the days of colour-light signals and electronic remote control that is being con-solidated now. The following are the dates at which these large mechanical installations were replaced by more modern equip-ment:

Paddington, G.W.R.	1935
Waterloo, S.R.	1936
Cannon Street, S.R.	1926
London Bridge, S.R.	1928
Manchester Victoria, L.M.S.	1929
Euston, L.M.S.	1951
Birmingham New Street, L.M.S.	1966
York, L.N.E.R.	1951
Edinburgh Waverley, L.N.E.R.	1936
Carlisle, L.M.S.	still mechanical

CHAPTER III

Track Circuiting

For many decades railways in Great Britain had been worked on
the principle that the signalman must see all the trains. The regulation of traffic lay not only in his hands so far as safety was concerned, but also in his judgment when questions of priority arose.
Signal-boxes were located at strategic points where the man could
have a good view of the line, and, in the few instances where
signals were beyond the view of the signalman, small electric-arm
repeaters were installed on the shelf that extended from one end of
each interlocking frame to the other. The signalman had to watch
the progress of trains through a junction and judge for himself the
right moment to replace signals to danger or to move points. The
facing-point lock-bar was there to prevent points from actually
being moved under a train, but the man's own eyes were his guide
as to when it was necessary to move points rapidly after a train
had passed. The siting of signal-boxes led to large numbers of very
picturesque structures. It was not always possible to build signal-
boxes at the lineside in a position that was a natural vantage point,
and so boxes were built on gantries spanning the tracks; above
station awnings; on viaducts; even in tunnels; and in one location
where a road was carried on a lofty arched bridge over a railway
which lay in a deep cutting a signal-box was placed in the upper
part of one of the arches. All this was delightful for the collector
of railway lore; and in more recent years beautifully executed
models have been made of some of these special erections. But as
the intensity of railway working grew and a clearer realization
emerged of the advantage to be derived from extending the area
under the control of one signal-box, it became evident that

something more than an ability merely to *see* the train was needed to help signalmen in going about their work.

The track circuit made fairly slow headway at first. Signal engineers steeped in traditional practice preferred to rely on mechanical appliances rather than incur the responsibility of maintaining track circuits in good order. As described in the foregoing chapter, some of the largest power signalling installations commissioned during the first decade of the present century had no track circuits at all. Where isolated track circuits were installed, largely for indication purposes, small electrically worked indicators were installed in the signal-boxes concerned. Yet the track circuit in its basic form is so simple, and so fundamentally safe in the protection it gives towards safe working of trains, that in retrospect it is difficult to understand why it was taken up so slowly. After all, there could not be anything much simpler than putting down insulated joints at each end of the section to be protected, connecting a battery across the rails at one end, and connecting a signalling relay across the rails at the far end. In those early days relays were very robust and reliable in operation. Today of course they are even more reliable, but a mere fraction of the original size and weight. The fact that a train on line cut off current to the relay and thereby opened certain circuits provided a classic fundamental example of the principle of 'fail-safe' which underlies all railway signalling practice. If for some reason current from the battery did not reach the relay it would not operate, and conditions were established as though there was a train on line. No signals could be cleared to allow a train to proceed. On the other hand, the construction of signalling relays is such as to make a failure on the danger side—that is, a relay sticking in a clear position—so remote as to be virtually negligible.

By the mid-1920s no one would dream of putting in a signalling installation of any size without track circuiting, and the change in attitude in the twelve years from 1910 to 1922 was in large measure due to the spectacular adoption of track circuiting on the Midland Railway following the collision at Hawes Junction on Christmas Eve 1910. On that occasion a whole chain of circumstances led up to the fatal move by the signalman Sutton in Hawes Junction box. There were several stages where different circumstances might have averted the fatal chain of events; but when all

37

else had failed a track circuit in one particularly vital spot would have saved the day; its absence set the seal on disaster.

The circumstances were these: Traffic was heavy during the night hours of December 23/24, and due to the policy of the Midland Railway of using large numbers of small locomotives and because of the extra holiday loadings, nearly every one of the numerous fast trains passing over the line between Leeds and Carlisle required to be double-headed on the mountain sections leading from south and north to Aisgill Summit. All these trains stopped at the summit to put off their assistant engines, because these latter were urgently required for other work at their home shed, either Carlisle or Hellifield. There was no means of turning them at Aisgill itself and so all these light engines had to make the journey, approximately three miles along the main line, from Aisgill box to Hawes Junction. There they were turned before proceeding back to their home stations. These engines came in ones and twos; sometimes they were coupled together, and on arrival at Hawes Junction many matters had to be sorted out between the drivers and the one signalman who was on duty. Some drivers wished to be given priority to get back to their home stations; others were almost due to be relieved, and the upshot of it was that Signalman Sutton in Hawes Junction box had an extremely busy night. At one time he had no less than nine light engines under his immediate control, and all the time more passenger and express goods trains were passing through on the main line. He was a fully experienced man and one who took a most conscientious and serious view of his responsibilities. He was, in other words, a first-class railwayman. Yet such was the pressure of events during the early hours of that Christmas Eve that at one stage he was guilty of an act of simple forgetfulness.

Two express passenger engines had been turned and were ready to proceed northwards to Carlisle. They were coupled together and as soon as a northbound express goods train had passed, Sutton signalled these two engines from the line where they were berthed on to the main line preparatory to allowing them to go forward as soon as the freight had cleared the three-mile section forward to Aisgill Summit. The two engines drew out on to the main line and stood some little distance short of the advanced starting signal. It was a dark night, at times with drizzling rain, and a strong wind was blowing from the west. In the darkness, relieved only by oil-lamps on the station and the occasional glare from locomotive fire-boxes, it was not possible to see very far from the signal-box. Steam was blowing about and Sutton was busy setting up movements for the various light engines to cross to the turntable road, to take water, and then to find paths for them to return to their home stations. Then at the height of all this busy-ness the most important northbound train of the night was due, the midnight sleeping-car express from St Pancras to Glasgow.

Amidst all his other duties the unfortunate man completely forgot the two engines that were standing at his advanced starting signal waiting to go to Carlisle. The drivers of these two engines were remiss in that they allowed themselves to be detained at that signal far longer than would have been necessary for the express freight train to pass Aisgill, and yet they did not obey the celebrated Rule 55, which requires that if a train is held at a signal for more than one minute the driver should send his fireman to the signal-box to remind the signalman of their presence. At Hawes Junction there was no mechanical aid to remind Signalman Sutton that the two engines were standing at his advanced starting signal. They passed completely out of his mind, and when the next box to the south offered the midnight express from St Pancras Sutton accepted it at once and offered it forward to Aisgill. The man in the latter box knew nothing about the two light engines that were waiting to go to Carlisle, and naturally assumed that the line was quite clear. He therefore accepted the midnight express and, having received his acceptance, Sutton pulled off all the Hawes Junction signals for the express. The men on the two light engines saw the advanced starting signal clear and started away, but unfortunately in a most leisurely fashion. They did not seem to be among the enginemen who were in a hurry that night to get back to their home station. Their leisurely start, and the fact that they soon became hidden from view from the south by passing through a short tunnel, meant that the express travelling at high speed very quickly caught them up. A bad collision followed, in which many lives were lost. Many factors had contributed to this accident near Hawes Junction, but despite everything else if there had been a track circuit at that advanced starting signal the presence of these engines would have been detected, and it would not have been possible for Sutton to pull off the signals for the midnight express.

Although the accident was not a very serious one, from the viewpoint of loss of life, it attracted widespread attention from the fact that it occurred on Christmas Eve, and also from the harrowing circumstances in which the victims met their deaths, imprisoned in the burning coaches. The Midland Railway Management took the whole affair extremely seriously. How seriously was at first not generally known, because at that time in railway history there was little in the way of publicity as we know it today; the action of the Midland Railway, though well known in higher railway circles, would probably have not been made public at all had there not occurred, in the autumn of 1913, a second collision, and fire, on the same stretch of line. On that second occasion a night express southbound from Carlisle ran into the rear of the preceding express on the final stage of the climb to Aisgill Summit. Public opinion was once again roused, and all the circumstances of the collision near Hawes Junction were recalled in the most vivid detail. It was not altogether surprising that certain commentators expressed the opinion that the Midland Railway had not profited by the lessons of Hawes Junction, otherwise a similar accident would not have occurred so near to the place of the first one, less than three years later.

It was in the enquiry into the Aisgill collision that Sir Guy Granet, General Manager of the Midland Railway, made a very comprehensive statement explaining the steps his company had taken after the first accident. He said to Sir John Pringle:

'You will remember, Sir, that most of the recommendations made in your report had reference to suggestions for minimizing the effects of accidents after they had taken place, and very important suggestions they were. But my Board, after very carefully considering your report, came to the conclusion that, beyond what you had recommended, it was very desirable to see whether it was not possible to take further steps to prevent the occurrence of accidents, or at any rate to make it more improbable that they should occur. You will remember that in the first accident it was admitted that it had occurred through two causes, both failures of the human element, namely: first the momentary forgetfulness of a signalman, a man of the highest character and record, who forgot that he had left two light engines on the road and subsequently admitted the express into that section; and second, owing to the failure of engine-drivers, also men of the highest record, to observe the provisions of Rule 55, under which they ought to have reminded the signalman of the presence of these light engines in the section. That source of weakness having been revealed, it was recognized that there were places on the line where it was possible, either through physical causes or possibly through density of traffic, for a signalman to forget the existence of a train standing at signals in his section, and so admit another one into it. Accordingly a survey of the line was made, and it was decided that in over 2,000 places the circumstances were such that it would be desirable to instal apparatus for correcting that tendency towards human error, and thereupon my Board made an order that apparatus should be provided at these places, and for the work to be put in hand at once. The apparatus decided upon was of a two-fold character. First of all there was the provision of track circuiting and electric locks, which has a two-fold effect. It has the effect of giving the signalman in his cabin a visible signal that there is a train in his section, and it also has the effect of preventing him, by means of electric locking, from improperly lowering his signals to admit a train into his section. Then, in addition to that it was decided to put in what is known as the "rotary interlocking block". This is a device which protects the other end of the section, or rather the section in the rear—it prevents the signalman in the rear from pulling off his signals and admitting a train into the section in advance until any train in that section has passed out of it. Well, in order to do that work, my Board immediately set aside, as a first instalment, the sum of £100,000 over and above the ordinary expenditure for maintenance, renewal and improvements, and ordered the work to be taken in hand at once, and that work has been proceeded with ever since as fast as possible. It cannot all be done at once: one obvious reason being the rate at which the locking of the signal lever frames can be altered, or added to, because the alterations in the locking cannot be done when traffic is about. Therefore, the whole of the work practically has to be done on Sundays; but special gangs have been put on, and have been continually at work at this since the order of the Board was given, with the result that we have today completed 374 track circuits and 379 rotary interlocking block installations. That leaves

41

still to be done 500 track circuits and 900 rotary interlocking block installations. I think, Sir, you have seen some of the work. I believe it is thoroughly satisfactory, and I believe that we have gone considerably beyond what any other railway company has done in the use of these devices.'

It can truly be said that the Hawes Junction accident did for track circuiting what the Armagh disaster of 1889 did for block working and automatic continuous brakes.

A track circuit is not merely a means of indicating the presence of a train. The contacts of a track relay are used to control the working of electric locks, which are applied to signal levers positively to prevent a lever being pulled if the track is occupied, or to prevent a pair of points being moved if a train is passing over them. Track circuits are essential for the operation of automatic signalling, and their use as a means of indicating the presence of trains is the foundation of the illuminated track diagram. From being a useful adjunct in the hey-day of mechanical signalling, the track circuit became the keystone of the arch—the very centrepiece of all modern signalling.

A little earlier in this chapter I stated that a track circuit was a very simple device. In its fundamental form it is so, particularly as in the Midland Railway case where traction was entirely steam and the length of individual track circuits was relatively short. They were operated by means of batteries, using direct current, and simple, massively constructed relays, operated again by direct current. As the art of track circuiting developed so complications grew. It was natural that track circuiting would be applied early to electric railways and in all the earliest British systems of electrification the return traction current passed through the running rails. Obviously, with heavy traction current passing through the rails, ordinary D.C. track-circuited current supplied by battery would be completely swamped and useless, and other means had to be devised. The practice of alternating-current track circuits was developing using relays which would be immune from the traction return currents passing in the rails. This is no place for a technical treatise on track circuits because the art has become a highly sophisticated one, providing signal engineers with a never-ending series of problems.

The introduction of alternating-current traction brought problems when track circuiting came to be applied to the electrified lines of the former London Brighton and South Coast Railway, and now that the standard British system of electric traction is at 25,000 volts a.c. special measures have had to be devised for making the signalling apparatus immune from the effects of stray currents arising from the traction system. Furthermore, the earliest track circuits, and indeed all track circuits installed until a very few years ago, relied upon insulated joints being made in the rails. Specially designed sets of insulating parts were inserted at the appropriate points, at actual joints in the rails, with insulations to fit the fish-plates and fishbolts. In recent years, however, the development of permanent way practice towards the installation of continuous-welded rails, with elimination of rail joints, and having virtually no break in the rails at all except at junction points, has provided another problem for the signal engineer. To meet this modern trend in permanent way practice various forms of jointless track circuit have been devised. I do not propose to go into the details of track circuiting practice, but have mentioned these various branches of the art of track circuiting to indicate how signalling techniques are constantly under review and development.

Track circuits as a means of indicating the presence of trains have played an outstanding part in the gradual development of control systems, not only at large stations and junctions, but over long stretches of main-line railway. The modern illuminated diagram depends entirely for its indication upon the working of track circuits. In its original application, on the London Underground Railways, the principle aimed at was to show all the tracks under the control of the particular signal-box as a continuous strip of light. The lamps were lit through circuits taken over the front, or energized contacts of the track circuit relay, so that when a train came on to the line the appropriate lamps would be extinguished and the length of track occupied by the train would appear dark. These early illuminated diagrams followed the fail-safe principle, in that if there was a track circuit failure and a relay was not ener-gized, or if a lamp burnt out, the diagram would show as if there were a train or a vehicle on the line; in other words, the danger indication would be shown. There were, however, certain practical difficulties towards this idea of a fail-safe indication on the illumin-ated diagram. In a large junction there would be many indication lamps, and by the very nature of railway working these lamps would be alight for much longer periods than they were extinguished. The illuminated diagrams thus became expensive in current consumption, while the continuous illumination of a large number of lamps meant that they got very hot and special provision had to be made for ventilation.

Consequently as the art of illuminated diagram design developed it was felt that the fail-safe principle need not be extended to the actual indications on the diagram. The working of the track circuits themselves would be sufficient safeguard against the setting up of wrong routes, or the clearing of signals in dangerous conditions; and so a change was made on the actual diagrams themselves to show the track circuits illuminated only when there was a train on the line. The lights on the diagram thus indicated the presence of a train, in contrast to having dark areas of extinguished lamps showing its presence as the principle was originally conceived. Furthermore the presence of a train could be indicated by a single lighted lamp, or pair of lamps, which made for considerable simplification of design as compared with the original idea of a strip of light. The development of the idea of illuminated track diagrams, together with power signalling, ended for all time the old requirement that a signalman must be able to *see* the entire area he controlled and watch the train movements. Whilst this revolution in practice was a little slow in coming on the main-line railways, some small though spectacular instances of control with the aid of illuminated diagrams were introduced on the London Underground railways, in several cases of which the signalmen did not see any actual trains at all during the course of their day's duty. Their observance of train movement was entirely through the aid of the illuminated track diagrams.

The value of track circuiting was demonstrated even more strikingly when consideration came to be given to installations of purely automatic signalling. Prior to this there had been certain installations where the operation of automatic signals was controlled by means of depression bars and electric treadles; but these did not provide the continuous protection that is afforded by track circuits in the event of a portion of a train breaking away, or in the event of some defect or obstruction on the line itself. The protection and proving that can be afforded by means of depression

44

bars or electric treadles is at the best of times no more than intermittent, whereas if a line is continuously track-circuited one has also continuous protection. The system of automatic signalling can be based entirely upon the simplest form of track circuit. The block sections are provided by the track circuits themselves, and an automatic signal controls the entrance to each track circuit, or block section. Unless the section is clear the circuits controlled by the track relay prevent the signal at the entrance to the track circuit being cleared. The principle can be readily extended to three-position signals or to even more elaborate systems, though the practice of multi-aspect signalling is discussed in greater detail in the next chapter.

The situation in regard to track circuiting at the beginning of the period under review was admirably summarized by Mr A. E. Tattersall, then Signal Superintendent of the Great Northern Railway, thus:

'Track circuiting *per se* cannot justly be described as a new system of railway signalling. It is really an adjunct to be applied to the existing system. There can be no doubt, in the light of present development, that it will also form the basis of future signalling systems, as in automatic signalling, or a system of automatic train control. It is capable of the widest application and enables far greater facilities to be provided to the benefit of traffic operation than was previously possible, and at the same time greatly increases the factor of safety. Where track circuiting is not in operation, the signalling of trains is entirely dependent on signalmen. The telegraph block is provided in order to assist the signalmen to carry out their duties efficiently, and in some instances is co-ordinated with the control of the fixed signals, as in what is termed 'lock and block' working. In neither case, however, does the indication conveyed by a signal at 'clear' guarantee that the whole of the section governed by such signal is unoccupied. Where track circuiting is in operation, and providing it extends throughout a section, it may be so arranged that the signal governing the section cannot show the 'clear' indication unless the whole of the section be clear, and should the section become occupied, the signal will be placed to 'danger' and kept in that position so long as any part of the section is occupied, and this quite independently of any action the signalman may take. Thus, the human element, as

45

represented by the signalman, is eliminated, and it will be generally conceded that the introduction of track circuiting marks the most important development in railway signalling since the adoption of the block system.'

CHAPTER IV

A New Conception—
Multi-Aspect Signalling

When I first entered the signalling profession in the summer of 1925, construction of semaphore signals of various types formed a major part of the manufacturing programme of most of the signalling firms in Great Britain. The four main-line railway groups all had large programmes of routine replacements of semaphore signals, not only entire bracket assemblies and gantries, but simple replacements of the arms themselves. Concurrently with this, in my own firm, large contracts were in hand for certain South American railways using three-position upper-quadrant semaphore signals. These were electro-pneumatically operated, and reference has already been made to the earlier installations in Great Britain of three-position upper quadrant signalling with electric mechanisms. There was every sign that upper-quadrant signalling might be coming into general use for new projects not only in South America, but also in Australia and New Zealand. All this was following the trend of development that had taken place in the USA some five to ten years earlier.

Colour-light signals were also in current production, but at that time they were not so numerous as semaphores. At that period they were regarded as an alternative to semaphores, rather than the signal of the future. Furthermore, the red-amber-green combination which is so familiar today, from its use also as a road traffic signal, was not by any means regarded as the only form of light signal to be considered. In the USA certain large railways had progressed a long way towards standardizing the position-light type of signal in which all the lenses were colourless and the indications were given as follows:

'Stop'—three white lights displayed horizontally

'Caution'—three white lights displayed diagonally
'All clear'—three white lights displayed vertically.

Some railways had even indulged in the elaboration of colour position-light signals, and all these American developments were being carefully studied by railway engineers and signalling manufacturers in Great Britain.

One feature of signalling practice at that time deserves special notice. It is that practice on the continent of Europe had not the slightest influence on developments in Great Britain. It is true that by the years 1923-4 the railways in the major industrial countries of Western Europe, such as France, Germany and Italy, were only just recovering from the ravages of World War I. There had been no time to initiate any large-scale forward planning; it was a case of getting the lines working again, and up to the standards that had prevailed before the war. There was an enormous amount of leeway to be made up, particularly in France and Germany. The only influence Continental practice had was in its continued use of the double-wire system of point and signal operation. This influence lay more in the direction of how British manufacturers could utilize such systems in remote localities, and in developing countries overseas, rather than of any consideration towards applying it on the home railways. There were a number of systems of power signalling in use on the Continent using various forms of interlocking machine; but these were generally considered to be a great deal more complicated than the power system which had already been developed in this country, and Continental influence generally at that time was so small as to be almost negligible.

The use of three-position semaphore signals began to open up a new concept of main-line signalling using automatic block. Hitherto the block sections on British main lines had been largely determined by the location of stations, junctions, intermediate level-crossings, and other points where it would be necessary at times to bring trains to a halt. The block sections along the line were inevitably of varying length as a result of this system, and, at times when trains were following close behind each other, delay could occur at the entrance to the longer sections because of the longer time necessary for preceding trains to clear the block ahead. On the other hand there were certain lines where points, crossings and other intersections with the main running lines scarcely

QUADRANT
SIGNALS

13. (left)
Two-position
electrics on the
Metropolitan

14. (right)
Three-position,
with calling-on
arms, at Ealing
Broadway, Great
Western Railway

CHANGE-OVER WORK ON THE SOUTHERN

Three Bridges cabin, with new frame, illuminated diagram and other equipment

ELECTRO-PNEUMATIC SIGNALS ON THE UNDERGROUND

16. (top) Tunnel signal, with air-worked spectacle

17. (left) Upper-quadrant shunt signal at Queen's Park

18. Under construction at Chippenham
   LONDON BRIDGE: 311 LEVERS
19. In service, in heavy traffic

existed, and yet on these lines traffic was heavy. They provided an ideal place for the installation of automatic block and with this the ordinary conception of a block post was discarded. Instead of having the traditional home signal at the block post, preceded by a distant signal, the block post consisted of nothing more than a single three-position signal. Such practice was nothing more nor less than a continuation of the practice embodied in the automatic signalling on the London and South Western Railway between Woking and Basingstoke referred to in the previous chapter, except that instead of having a two-armed signal at each block post there was a single arm displaying any one of three aspects.

On a line including no points and crossings, a succession of three-position signals working automatically, controlled by track circuits, provided a very simple and indeed elegant solution. If one section ahead was clear, and the one beyond that occupied, the signal at the entrance to a section would be in the 'caution' position with its arm inclined diagonally upwards; if at least two sections ahead were clear the arm would be in the 'all-clear' position, pointing vertically upwards. This principle was used in the signalling of the Ealing and Shepherds Bush Railway, using electrically operated three-position upper-quadrant signals. These signals had spectacle plates containing three coloured roundels to provide the night indications—red for 'stop', amber for 'caution' and green for 'all-clear'.

With the introduction of three-position upper-quadrant signals, and the existence prior to December 1922 of a large number of independent and highly individualistic railway companies in Great Britain, there was every possibility of wide divergencies in practice being developed on the railways according to the precepts of the various signal engineers. Furthermore, while some engineers were convinced that three-position signalling was likely to be the standard for the future, some men of an older generation resisted it strongly and expressed in no uncertain terms their conviction that the existing system using two-position lower-quadrant signals, either singly or in groups, was the best that could be devised. This point is an appropriate one to introduce into this account of British railway signalling development one of the greatest thinkers and greatest personalities of the inter-war period — Arthur Ewart Tattersall.

D

Tattersall entered the signalling profession on the Lancashire and Yorkshire Railway, and as early as 1906 he had gone to Ireland to take up the position of Chief Assistant to the Signal Superintendent of the Great Southern and Western Railway. His stay in Ireland was brief, for in the following year he was appointed Signal and Electrical Assistant to the Chief Engineer of the Metropolitan Railway, and remained in that capacity for fourteen years. He then became Signal Superintendent of the Great Northern, and it was in this capacity that he read a paper to The Institution of Railway Signal Engineers on 'Three-position signalling'. He had introduced two-position upper-quadrant signals on the Metropolitan Railway and on the Great Northern he planned the introduction of three-position upper-quadrant signals on a considerable scale. At the time of the grouping however, in January 1923, when the Great Northern, together with the Great Central and the Great Eastern came into the southern area of the L.N.E.R., Tattersall became Assistant Signal Engineer of the Southern Area, while A. F. Bound of the Great Central became Signal Engineer. This was not a happy partnership. At this distance in time it can be revealed that Bound and Tattersall never really got on together, and in later years when both of them had moved elsewhere on British railways a considerable antagonism developed between them. This was never more clearly shown than when Tattersall read a paper on signalling to The Institution of Civil Engineers in 1942.

Tattersall's paper to The Institution of Railway Signal Engineers, in 1921, was read while he was still on his own, on the Great Northern, and to use a colloquialism that paper 'started something'. Tattersall's plea for the establishment of greater logic in signal aspects, and for a standard code of practice with three-position signals to be established on a national basis, was taken up enthusiastically by the majority of the members present at the reading of the paper, and as a result the Institution itself set up what was called the 'Three-position Signal Committee'. Bound, as one of the senior signal officers on British railways, and a senior member of the Institution, was elected Chairman, and the members of the Committee consisted of four railwaymen and three prominent signal manufacturing contractors. The railwaymen concerned were W. Challis, who was then Signal Superintendent of the Metropolitan Railway; W. S. Every, Signal Engineer of the London Underground railways; Tattersall himself; and W. J. Thorrowgood, Signal and Telegraph Engineer of the London and South Western Railway. The contractors were S. L. Glenn, Manager of the British Power Railway Signal Company, manufacturers of the low-pressure pneumatic system; T. S. Lascelles, of the W. R. Sykes Interlocking Signal Company; and H. M. Proud, of the Westinghouse Brake and Saxby Signal Company, as that firm was then known.

At that time it was very interesting to find the signal engineer of the North Eastern Railway strongly in opposition to the idea of three-position signals at all. Arthur Hurst was one of the elder statesmen of the profession, and he represented a railway which at the time had probably installed more power signalling than any other company, all on the electro-pneumatic system. The North Eastern also probably held another record, that of maximum number of semaphore arms per route mile of railway. The use of arms on the North Eastern had always been extraordinarily lavish, and great care was taken to position these arms in the precise location required by the Traffic Department, irrespective of what elaborate structures might be needed to carry them. The North Eastern was as lavish with its structures as it was with its semaphores, and, during the discussion that led up to the establishment of the three-position Signal Committee by The Institution of Railway Signal Engineers, Arthur Hurst expressed his misgivings as follows:

'Our present system of signalling is not liable to be mistaken. You introduce five cases which are liable to be mistaken by a driver. Surely that is an element of danger quite enough to condemn the whole system. It seems to me that the object of three-position signalling is to get over a difficulty in crowded parts of the line, probably nearer large towns, and so forth, where you have got to get a large amount of traffic over the line in a short time. That is a system the idea of which is to give the driver additional facilities, in order to let him run a little quicker and get over the line in a shorter time, and allow more trains to occupy the line. Clearly, that does not apply to the open country.'

He went on:

'The idea of three-position signals in the United States began with the wrong idea altogether. It began with the idea of controlling the trains for speeds rather than controlling them for routes; and where you try to control a train for speed, and tell the driver by means of signal at what speed he is to run, you always have this difficulty that in the absence of a signal from any cause whatever—light out, signal blown down, or any other circumstances—you deceive the driver so that he runs at a speed at which he ought not to, and there is a very grave element of danger. I do not want to condemn three-position signals, because they may be found necessary, and may be altered to such a degree that the difficulties and uncertainties may be eliminated, and the signals become of very great practical value.'

The tide was however running strongly in favour of three-position signals and the Committee began its activities with the general approval of a large majority of the members of the profession. The work of the Committee extended over more than two years and although it was set up in March 1922 its report was not issued until December 1924. In the meantime a very important event had taken place. The first day colour-light signals to be installed in Great Britain had been commissioned in 1920 on the Liverpool Overhead Railway. That installation was not however regarded as of any great significance at the time because the special conditions on 'The Overhead' were generally deemed to warrant something special in the way of signalling. The really significant development took place in 1923. In readiness for the traffic expected to result from the opening of the British Empire Exhibition at Wembley in 1924, the L.N.E.R. put in a special loop line to facilitate the running of a shuttle service of trains between Marylebone and the Exhibition station. Traffic was expected to be heavy and, in addition to the Exhibition loop itself, provisions were made for close headway working on the main line between Marylebone and Neasden Junction.

In this five-mile stretch of the former Great Central Railway there were no intermediate passenger stations and no points and crossings. The location was ideal for automatic signalling, and on Bound's recommendation a system of three-position automatic signalling was designed and installed. The main point, however, was that these signals were not semaphores at all, but colour-lights. Some of the actual signals themselves were of the 'Hall' type with three-position relay mechanisms in the signal head and capable of displaying either red, amber or green indications through the one lens, while others were of the multi-lens type, having the control relay in a case alongside. This was the first installation of colour-light signals on a main-line railway anywhere in Great Britain and it came in for a great amount of attention, particularly having regard to the fact that its designer was chairman of the Three-Position Signal Committee of The Institution of Railway Signal Engineers.

This installation demonstrated to British railway operating men that it was possible to provide satisfactory indications by light signals, for main-line fast running, that were clearly visible at long range in strong sunlight. This result was achieved by using a system of two lenses, the outer one being colourless and the inner one red, green or amber as required. The lenses were so designed as to give a very concentrated beam of light from a lamp placed precisely at the focus point of this binary system. It is true that finality in design of the lens and lamp system was not by any means achieved in this first installation; in fact the lens systems of colour-light signals are still the subject of considerable research work even today. But the principle was demonstrated, and the day colour-light signal was immediately recognized as having an immeasurable superiority, for 'three-position' signalling, over the power-operated semaphore signal working in the upper quadrant and displaying three positions: horizontal, inclined upwards, and vertically upwards, for 'stop', 'caution' and 'proceed' respectively. In the colour-light signal there were no moving parts, and the same indication was given by night and by day.

All the argument and controversy surrounding the introduction of three-position upper-quadrant semaphores was avoided, and one hardly needs to add that a simple case containing nothing but lenses and electric lamps was very much cheaper than a substantial electric or electro-pneumatic mechanism such as that required for operation of three-position upper-quadrant semaphore signals. It became generally recognized that it was the colour-light signal rather than the three-position upper-quadrant semaphore signal that was the signal of the future, and the deliberations of the Three-Position Signal Committee of The Institution of Railway Signal Engineers henceforth became generally directed towards the establishment of a code of practice in which colour-light signals would form the sole basis. In this respect, however, the Committee was not unanimous. One member, Mr S. L. Glenn, stood out strongly against the majority view, and when the time came for the Committee to make its report to the Institution he submitted a minority report, in which he argued strongly the case for the three-position upper-quadrant semaphore signal.

Taking the history of three-position signalling many years forward, it must be recorded that not all administrations favoured the use of the multi-lens type of signal. A strong body of opinion favoured the single-light-unit type, in which the control relay was housed in the signal itself and carried in its vane three coloured roundels. The movement of the vane, in response to the respective energization of the relay coils, brought one or other of the coloured roundels into the lamp and lens unit of the signal, and caused either a red, green or amber light to be displayed according to the position of the relay. With multi-aspect signalling there had to be a relay. The difference was that it was housed separately and the appropriate lamps in the signal lighted according to its movement. Those who argued for the single-lens type of colour-light signal, nowadays generally referred to as the 'searchlight' type, were concerned with the very concentrated beam of light thrown from a daylight colour-light signal. With the usual arrangement of lenses as installed on the Marylebone – Neasden section of the L.N.E.R., the green lens was twenty-two inches above the red, with the amber placed intermediately. While the beams from the various lens units could be focused independently it was felt that something of the advantage of the concentrated beam was lost if that beam, for different indications, came from different positions in the signal. With only one lens unit the signal could be focused horizontally to coincide with the normal eye level of the driver, whereas the uppermost one would have to be inclined slightly downwards. As previously mentioned, the Marylebone – Neasden installation included both single units and multi-lens colour-light signal, and at first British opinion veered strongly towards the multi-lens system.

At this stage it is well to pause and pay tribute to the engineers and operating officers of the former Great Central Railway for the leading part they played in the adoption of an innovation that was to prove a turning point in the history of British railway signalling. The Great Central line was certainly not the first to instal colour-light signals anywhere in the world; but the installation came at a time when British signalling practice, from being very largely standardized, had, by common consent of most of the leading figures in the profession, turned into a phase of rapid evolution.

The majority of the signals on the Marylebone – Neasden section were automatics and the operating rules provided for the following procedure: if the driver of a train came to any one of these signals and found it in the danger position the procedure was that in such a case he would wait for one minute and then proceed cautiously, keeping a sharp look-out, and at such a speed that he could stop short of any obstruction that might be sighted ahead. It was appreciated that the signal might be at danger for one of two reasons: there might be a track circuit failure which would prevent the signal clearing, or there might be a train ahead or an obstruction on the line which had caused the track circuit to become de-energized. Unfortunately, of course, there are always drivers whose judgment in special cases of this kind is not equal to the occasion. There was one case where a driver's idea of 'proceeding cautiously' involved a speed in excess of 40 m.p.h. in fog. The signal showing red, from which he had restarted, was protecting a train in the section, and the result was a collision—fortunately not too serious. The occurrence did, however, give rise to considerable discussion and rethinking among railway operating men and signal engineers, in conjunction with the Inspecting Officers of the Ministry of Transport. But it was not until many years later that the present system of operating with signal post telephone was adopted generally. This practice will be described in its normal historical sequence in this book.

Although it is a slight digression from the subject of railway signalling, it is worth mentioning that at this time, in 1925, the first installation of colour-light road traffic signals was made in Piccadilly, London, at the junction with St James's Street. The signals used were of the railway main-line type designed for long-range viewing, and they had, for the first time on a highway, the now familiar red, amber and green lights indicating 'stop', 'be prepared' and 'go'. Railway practice was followed to the extent of having a miniature lever frame installed on an island in the middle of the road, in a tiny cabin, and worked by a policeman. This installation was brought into service in the summer of 1926 at a time when many attempts were being made to swim the English

Channel. The installation in Piccadilly led to a humorous cartoon being published in the *Daily Express*.

Although this installation was of great historic interest in view of all the developments in road traffic signalling that followed from it, the main-line railway type of colour-light signal was not ideal for the purpose. As one commentator remarked at the time, the signals looked fine if you viewed them from Hyde Park Corner, but they became progressively worse as you drew nearer to them. The binary lens system with its concentrated beam was unsuitable for road use, for which one did not require long-range sighting, but a wide spread of the light, maintaining maximum visibility up to the last minute of approach. Since then, of course, special signals have been developed for road traffic purposes, and every motorist is familiar enough with their effectiveness even in the brightest sunshine. At that time better results would probably have been obtained by straight improvization from one of the less sophisticated types of railway colour-light signal rather than the high-speed main-line type. These latter had eight-inch outer lenses; but a very effective smaller version with six-inch lenses was used in the tunnels of the Metropolitan Railway, and this would probably have given quite good results on the highway, though not equalling, of course, the highly developed road signals in use today.

In referring to tunnel signals, however, it must be explained that with any form of colour-light signal other than the searchlight type there is a danger of a misleading indication being given by what are termed 'phantoms'. The sun shining on the outer lens of a signal can, at certain angles of inclination, produce a reflection that gives an impression that the signal is alight, even though the coloured lens is inside and separated by a short distance from the outer lens. In my earlier days in the profession I remember most vividly the numerous experiments that were taking place, both optically and by the insertion of various physical shield devices, to eliminate the risk of 'phantom' indications. With a single-lens system, such as that used in the tunnel signals of the Metropolitan, the risk of 'phantoms' would be still greater, as the sun could shine directly on a coloured glass. It was, of course, for this reason that the main-line type of signal was chosen for the inaugural road installation in Piccadilly.

Although light signals were in fairly common use, not only on the Metropolitan but on other underground lines in London, those rapid-transit, electrically-worked railways have not, even to this day, adopted multi-aspect colour-light signalling. Their colour-light signalling has always been based on the old concept of a 'home' signal, demanding a 'stop' when it is in the danger position, and a 'distant' or 'repeater' leading up to it. Consequently the signalling on these underground lines has always been of two-aspect rather than three-aspect units.

CHAPTER V

The Relationship of Signalling to Brake Power— Introduction of the Fourth Aspect

During the deliberations of the Three-position Signal Committee, or, as it later became known, and more correctly, 'The Three-aspect Signal Committee', the question arose as to how the new principles being evolved would deal with specific instances in stations and yards where signals were required to protect points, crossings, and other conflicting movements, but where the distance between successive signals, on account of the track configurations, would be very short. With mechanical signalling such instances had been dealt with by the installation of distant signal arms covering a number of home signals. By keeping the distant signals at danger, the speed of an approaching train could be materially reduced, and where extreme caution was required the home signals could be lowered sequentially, bringing the train slowly forward from one to another until the sections of the line became clear. Under the new code of aspects, however, the principle was very simply defined, namely, that a red should be preceded by an amber, and an amber by green. The simplicity of this arrangement had so strong an appeal that variations to suit local conditions were in those early days not considered admissible.

At this stage it is important to appreciate the basic relationship between the spacing of signals and the aspects they display, and the brake power of the trains using the line. With mechanical signalling the fundamental principle regarding the location of a distant signal was that full braking distance for the fastest train should be provided between the post carrying the distant signal and the signal next ahead which might be showing the danger indication. Naturally the distant signals had to be spaced to provide safe working for the fastest trains, but even at that stage in the evolution of railway operation there were great discrepancies between the brake capacity of different trains on the line. An express passenger train fitted with continuous brakes throughout would require a definite distance to come to a dead stop from an initial speed of, shall we say, 75 m.p.h. That distance would be increased in a falling gradient and reduced on a rising gradient. Against this three other cases of different braking capacity can be quoted, namely:

1. An express goods train with all vehicles fitted with the continuous brake and limited to a maximum speed of 60 m.p.h.

2. A partially fitted goods train with some of the vehicles fitted with the continuous brake, the remainder piped and the brake-van at the rear connected to the continuous brake system.

3. A loose-coupled train, on which the only brake power was that of the engine and tender and of the guard's brake-van.

In mechanical signalling days the spacing of the distant signal was something of a compromise. The braking distances for an express passenger train from an initial speed of 75 m.p.h. could be considered as roughly the same as that of a loose-coupled goods from an initial speed of 30 m.p.h., and the intermediate classes of freight train, by the limitation of their maximum speeds, would fall very much into the same stopping-distance group. It provided a rough and ready solution which served very well for scores of years on steam-operated main lines. Various refinements may also be mentioned at this stage because they all have an effect on stopping distance. At one time it was the practice to apply brakes to all the wheels of a locomotive; but the work of maintaining brakes on bogie wheels, with the necessary flexible connections from the main part of the engine, and equally upon trailing trucks, was not really worth the extra cost involved, having regard to the additional brake power provided on the locomotive.

It was about the year 1925 that this breakaway from the refinement in braking took place. It had the effect of making the locomotive, to use a colloquialism, the 'worst-braked' vehicle in the train, in that a proportion of its total weight was unbraked. The result of this was to have an effect upon the stopping distance of express trains. The carriages would be braked in exact proportion to their weight, so that if one had a certain class of engine with a light train, its stopping distance from a certain initial speed would be less than with the same class of engine working a heavy train. An exact instance taken from the practice of the G.W.R. will make this quite clear. Tests were made with a 'Castle' class 4-6-0 loco-motive with trains of six and twelve coaches respectively. At 60 m.p.h. the stopping distance from an emergency application was 540 yards with a twelve-coach train, and 580 yards with a six-coach train. At 80 m.p.h. the distances were 1,060 yards with a twelve-coach train and 1,150 yards with a six-coach train—nearly 100 yards or ten per cent. difference at 80 m.p.h.

Of course the question of braking distance in relation to the spacing of signals can, in practice, depend very much upon the extent to which a driver could see a signal before he actually came up level with it. The driver who was fully alert, and who was favoured with good weather, would undoubtedly take immediate steps to reduce the speed of his train the moment he sighted an adverse signal, and therefore, as regards stopping distance, he would have a comfortable margin in hand. In contrast to present-day conditions with road traffic signals, a driver on the railway who sights a distant signal clear can proceed at full speed in the firm understanding that the road is clear and will remain so. Only the direst emergency could lead to a signal being thrown to danger or caution in a driver's face. This, of course, is in complete contrast to road conditions, where nowadays if one sights a traffic signal showing green there is always the chance, and in some cases, the strong probability that it will change to red before one reaches it! On the railway, however, the advanced sighting of signals is always regarded as a bonus. Full braking distance for the fastest trains must always be provided from the distant signal post to the home signal next ahead.

While the Three-aspect Signal Committee of The Institution of Railway Signal Engineers was to a large extent concerned with main-line cases where the incidence of points and crossings pre-cluded anything but short spacing of signals, its immediate problem was not so much that of fast-running main lines as of the inten-sively-used suburban line. Two members of the Committee, Messrs W. J. Thorrowgood and W. Challis, had on their hands an imme-diate problem in providing new signalling for sections of the Southern Railway that were to be electrified in the very near future. Authorization had been given for the electrification of the former South Eastern and Chatham lines running in to the London terminal stations of Blackfriars, St Paul's, Cannon Street, and Charing Cross. Following the introduction of three-position upper-quadrant semaphore signalling and electric point operation on the Chatham side of Victoria Station, plans had already been con-sidered in outline for the resignalling of Charing Cross on similar principles. Estimates and preliminary drawings of signal configura-tions had already been prepared. But by the time the plans for electrification had reached the stage of detailed proposals for the new signalling, the Three-aspect Signal Committee had already decided among its own members that the colour-light, rather than the upper-quadrant semaphore, would be the signal of the future in Great Britain. Therefore the new work on the South Eastern lines in London was all planned on the basis of multi-aspect colour-light signals.

Although the original work was confined to the innermost areas, covering the immediate approaches to Blackfriars and St Paul's and the lines between London Bridge and Charing Cross and Cannon Street respectively, the engineers of the Southern Railway and their colleagues on the Three-aspect Signal Committee fortunately looked a great deal beyond these inner areas where speeds were necessarily quite low. They had equally in mind the extension of the colour-light signalling outwards from London Bridge on the former South Eastern main line, and no less, of course, the ultimate equipment of both the Brighton and the South Western suburban lines with signalling on similar principles. In so doing the problem of signal in relation to brake power of the trains assumed a most acute form.

Taking the South Eastern lines in particular, on the main line to Tonbridge, the suburban stations were spaced close together, with New Cross, St John's, Hither Green, Grove Park, Elmstead Woods, Chislehurst, and Orpington in rapid succession. Suburban trains would require to follow each other at close intervals during the morning and evening rush hours, and yet at other times the line had to provide for express passenger trains to and from coastal resorts with which speeds of 75 m.p.h. and even 80 m.p.h. were not uncommon descending the bank from Elmstead Woods tunnel to Hither Green. If a system of three-aspect colour-light signals had been laid out to provide full braking distance between successive signals for these Kent Coast express trains, the signal spacing on the fastest-running stretches would have needed to be around 1,500 yards. One has to provide for a normal rather than an emergency brake application. With the multiple-unit electric trains which it was planned to use for the suburban services, maximum speeds between stations were not expected to exceed 55 m.p.h. Furthermore the electric trains were to be fitted with the Westinghouse brake, which generally gives shorter stopping distances than the vacuum from comparable speeds. A signal spacing which had to provide safe working for these Kent Coast expresses would thus have seriously handicapped those planning an intense service of electric multiple-unit trains fitted with the Westinghouse brake.

Faced with this problem, the Committee of The Institution of Railway Signal Engineers reached an extremely simple, yet elegant solution by the introduction of a fourth aspect. This took the form of the double yellow, and immediately provided for maximum usage of the line by two dissimilar classes of trains. The sequence of aspects now became red, single yellow, double yellow, green, and the spacing of successive signals along the line was based on the following premise: the driver of an express train travelling at between 70 and 80 m.p.h. upon sighting any colour-light signal aspect other than green, would immediately take steps to reduce the speed of his train, and full braking distance for the fastest train on the line would be provided between the double yellow and the red. On the other hand the driver of a suburban electric train, never travelling at more than 55 m.p.h. and having an extremely effective brake, could virtually use the double yellow as his 'all-clear' knowing that he had adequate distance to stop between the single yellow and the red. The question of speed in relation to stopping distance was not only the difference between multiple-unit electric trains and steam-locomotive-hauled trains. The tests on the G.W.R. previously referred to showed that with a twelve-coach train and a 'Castle' class engine, the emergency stopping distance from a speed of 60 m.p.h. was 540 yards, whereas from 80 m.p.h. it was 1,060 yards—very nearly double the distance from 80 m.p.h. than from 60 m.p.h. In the solution arrived at by the Three-aspect Signal Committee the use of the double yellow did virtually double the warning distance for a high-speed train.

When the report of the Three-aspect Signal Committee was presented to The Institution of Railway Signal Engineers it was only natural that there should be some discussion as to the rightness of the aspects that were recommended, particularly with regard to the totally new aspect of 'double yellow'. It is important at this stage to recall that in British railway semaphore signalling practice the yellow light was quite exceptional at that time, and not in general use as the night 'caution' indication of a distant signal. Until the grouping of the railways in 1923, the great majority of lines showed no difference at night between the indication of a 'distant' and of a 'stop' signal. The driver could sight a red, in the blackness of the night, and it would be entirely up to his knowledge of the road to decide whether it was a 'distant' or a 'home' signal that he was approaching. It is extraordinary that this anomaly was accepted for so many years and that it prevailed without resulting in any serious accidents.

One can only look back with intense admiration to the diligence and expertness of the British locomotive engine-driver of that period. I have heard it said of some drivers that they could find their way to their destination blindfold, so intimately did they know every sound and 'feel' of the line they were traversing. Only a few railways made an attempt to distinguish between the night indication of 'distant' and 'stop' signals. The London Brighton and South Coast railway mounted the Coligny-Welch distinguishing lamp beside their distants. This gave an illuminated fish-tail indication to the right of the distant signal lamp. By far the most arresting of all distinguishing marks for distant signals was that standardized on the Furness Railway, which used flashing reds operated by acetylene gas and controlled in the same way as a winking navigational buoy. In the days when my home was at Barrow-in-Furness I used to see these flashing red distant signals at night, and they gave a remarkably distinctive indication.

With the coming of the amber light in three-aspect colour-light signals and the general acceptance in these signals of amber as the 'caution' indication, it was of course a logical step to change the night indication of all distant signals, whether colour-light or semaphore, to amber, and this change was gradually made over the entire country. Although the actual colour is more truly amber, the caution is now always referred to as 'yellow' and will be called so from now onwards in this book. At the same time the painting of the semaphores themselves was changed from red to yellow and the chevron became black. With this change came a new night indication, namely, green over yellow, in place of the previous green over green, or green over red from a distant signal mounted beneath a stop signal and slotted with it. With this change came the view among certain British railwaymen that with colour-light signalling the first warning should not have been an entirely new aspect, namely, double yellow; instead it should have been green over yellow in conformity with the night aspects of slotted semaphore signals when the home arm was clear and the distant at 'caution'.

The Committee had very clearly in mind however the great principle underlying all signal engineering, that of 'fail-safe', and one has always to legislate for the possibility of failure. In a two-light indication such as double yellow, or green over yellow, there is always the possibility that one or other of the lamps might burn out. If that lamp happened to be the yellow in a 'green over yellow' aspect, the driver would immediately be given a less restrictive indication. He would be given a single green which, in colour-light practice, means 'proceed at full speed', instead of the more restrictive green over yellow, which would be leading towards a colour-light signal at single yellow, followed by a red. If, on the other hand, one of the lamps in a double-yellow combination burnt out, the aspect would be changed from the double yellow to single yellow, and thus become more restrictive. The safety feature was thus completely reversed from that of the green over yellow, and in this respect, if for no other, the double yellow was greatly to be preferred to the green over yellow.

The sequence of aspects in a four-aspect signalling system now seems so logical and so simple that it is difficult to appreciate, nowadays, why there should have been any controversy at the time of their first introduction. Furthermore the almost unanimous decision of the Committee to concentrate on colour-light signals and to rule out semaphores made the introduction of a fourth aspect quite easy, whereas to do the same with semaphores would, of course, have involved the use of two-arm configurations at every signal location where a fourth aspect was required. It is also very important to appreciate the inestimable value of the work done by the Three-aspect Signal Committee in establishing the aspects they did. Those aspects have stood the test of time, through all the

Insell-Ferriera Route Working Frame at Newport West

GREAT WESTERN DEVELOPMENT

334-lever all-electric interlocking frame, at Cardiff West

GREAT
WESTERN
SEMA-
PHORES

22. Reading East Main : Group including route indicating

23. Reading West Main : Group with 'slip' distants for

One of the earliest three-aspect signals:
G.C.R. Marylebone – Neasden line

25. Four-aspect signal with
projector-type route indicator,
Salford, L.M.S.R.

COLOUR-LIGHT SIGNAL EVOLUTION

COLOUR-LIGHT SIGNAL
EVOLUTION

26. (*left*)
'Speed' signals at Mirfield, L.M.S.R.

27. (*right*)
Modern four-aspect signal, with
directional high-speed route
indicator, Potters Bar, British
Railways, Eastern Region

formative years of colour-light signalling between 1925 and the launching of the British Railways Modernization Plan in 1955. All the intensive work done since 1955 has been based without exception upon the code of signal aspects evolved by that Committee of The Institution of Railway Signal Engineers, which in its very simplicity has fulfilled all requirements up to the present time. Travelling on the continent of Europe and seeing how other countries have developed colour-light signalling practice, with a multiplicity of units and indications which can be confusing to the uninitiated, it is very gratifying to realize that we in Great Britain were the pioneers of multi-aspect signalling using more than three indications, and that the very simple four-aspect signalling system devised more than forty years ago is today handling with brilliant success the operation on the electrified main line of the London Midland Region of British Railways between Euston and Crewe— one of the fastest, and certainly the most intensively worked main line in Europe.

Although it is stepping some ten years beyond the deliberations and conclusions of the Three-aspect Signal Committee, the value of their work applied in a different sphere was demonstrated most vividly on the main line of the North Eastern area of the L.N.E.R. between York and Northallerton in 1935. A few years earlier extensive civil engineering works had been undertaken on that important line to improve traffic working facilities, by the laying in of additional running lines and long running loops; and to improve the working still further colour-light signalling had been installed throughout from Skelton Junction, just to the north of York itself, to Northallerton. The traffic flowing over that line was of a varied kind, ranging in speed from the East Coast expresses normally running at a maximum of about 75 m.p.h., down to heavy mineral trains, which, in the most favourable circumstances, rarely exceeded 30 m.p.h. Between these extreme categories were the intermediate classes of passenger and goods trains and one had, as described earlier in this chapter, a rough compromise between maximum running speeds and available brake power. The colour-light signals, which were all of the searchlight type, displayed three aspects and they were spaced on an average 1,300 yards apart. This provided for a three-minute headway between express passenger trains running at a speed of about 65 m.p.h., and with the practice that then prevailed of running express trains in closely defined groups it enabled a maximum number of trains to be passed through in a minimum amount of time, then leaving considerable intervals for the slower-moving freight trains to progress. The improvement in operation was very marked and the installation as a whole, in conjunction with the improved track facilities that had been provided, was considered an outstanding success.

Then in the year 1935 the Silver Jubilee streamlined high-speed express was introduced, running between King's Cross and Darlington non-stop at an average speed of 70 m.p.h. With the very powerful 'A4' class Pacific locomotives, and a train of no more than 230 tons behind the tender, this new streamlined train was capable of speeds of between 90 and 100 m.p.h. on level track, and over the York – Northallerton section an immediate problem was created by the adverse relationship of signalling to brake power. The Pacific locomotives, like their predecessors of the non-streamlined 'A3' class, were only braked to 60 per cent of their total loaded weight, and the tender was only braked to 65 per cent of its weight when fully loaded with coal and water. The engine braking is explained by the fact that neither the bogie nor the trailing truck was braked, while of course the tender would have to be braked to no more than its weight when a large proportion of the coal and water had been used up. If it were braked to 100 per cent of its full loaded weight it would have been over-braked when supplies had been depleted, with the danger of wheels picking up. Comparing The Silver Jubilee with The Flying Scotsman, for example, one had in the first case a locomotive of 165 tons and a train of 230 tons, in the latter the same locomotive with a trailing load of 500 tons at least. The proportion of unbraked weight was thus very much higher in The Silver Jubilee than in The Flying Scotsman, and it so happened that the faster running of all trains over the York – Northallerton section is made in the south-bound direction where the tenders would be almost fully loaded. In both cases the locomotives took over their workings with fully-loaded tenders at Newcastle.

The working of the new high-speed train was limited to a nominal maximum throughout between King's Cross and Newcastle to 90 m.p.h. In the setting of any such limits, however, one has to provide for a margin in each direction to cover slight inaccuracies in instruments, and no less in the judgment of individual drivers; and it was realized that in actual practice this new train could be expected to run at 100 m.p.h. on certain sections of the line — although such running was not encouraged by the authorities and would lead to reprimand of the drivers if it occurred at all frequently. Nevertheless, the clear possibility of that light streamlined train running at 100 m.p.h. between York and Northallerton had definitely to be legislated for. Over the southern part of the line between York and London the signalling was semaphore throughout with manual block, and to provide adequate stopping distances the train was double-blocked throughout; in other words, 'line clear' was not given until at least two block sections were clear. This could be arranged by special instructions, but no such provision could be made between York and Northallerton with three-aspect colour-light signalling, and many of the sections working automatically.

When the train was first introduced, therefore, it was somewhat ironical that over the best running section of the whole line between London and Newcastle speed had to be limited to 70 m.p.h. in order not to exceed the limits of safe braking with the existing signal spacing. In the meantime however, a very simple and effective solution to this difficulty was available, by merely adding to the existing searchlight signals a separate light unit on the top to change them all into four-aspect signals. The searchlight signal mechanism provided the green, yellow and red indications from the single lens of the original units, and the additional light unit mounted on the top was lighted when it was necessary to give the double yellow. Changing the signals from three-aspect to four-aspect increased the distance between the first warning, the double yellow, to the signal showing red from the original 1,300 yards to 2,600 and immediately provided amply adequate braking distance for the Silver Jubilee when running at its maximum speed.

This was indeed a classic instance of the relationship between signal location and brake power, and as such a most graphic example of the use of the fourth aspect.

CHAPTER VI

Colour-light Signalling on the Southern Railway

It is one thing for a committee to hold a succession of meetings, and with almost complete unanimity to formulate principles. No matter how expert the members of such a committee may be, or how essentially practical their outlook, it is quite another thing to apply such principles to the physical task of signalling a railway. The first instance of three-aspect colour-light signalling in Great Britain was made on the simplest possible kind of railway, on a section of plain line with no intermediate stations and nothing in the way of points and crossings. The only complications on the line between Marylebone and Neasden, and on the Exhibition loop, were purely technical matters concerning the working of the track circuits in the long tunnels between Marylebone Goods Yard and Canfield Place. The earliest installation of four-aspect colour-light signals were made on lines totally different, in fact, on some of the busiest and most complicated stretches of railway in the entire London Metropolitan area. The very first installation, on the old Chatham line leading to St Paul's, was not easy. But the second installation, covering the approaches to Cannon Street and Charing Cross, was exceptionally difficult.

Had the old layout at Cannon Street remained, things would have been even worse. In earlier days the South Eastern Railway, and later the South Eastern and Chatham Management Committee, seemed to foster and intensify the inherent difficulties in working a stretch of line which fed two terminal stations on the opposite side of the River Thames. In the case of many long-distance trains it was the practice to proceed into Cannon Street first, then reverse direction and take the western side of the Borough Market triangle and terminate in Charing Cross.

Continental boat expresses used to start from Charing Cross and then go into Cannon Street to pick up the mail portions; then after attaching a fresh engine at what was originally the rear of the train they would proceed via London Bridge to Dover or Folkestone. All this involved a plethora of light-engine and crossing movements that were conducive to much delay, especially when long-distance trains performing these evolutions were run in the middle of the suburban rush hours. Things became somewhat simplified after World War I, when the Continental workings were concentrated at Victoria rather than Charing Cross and Cannon Street, and the only Continental workings from Cannon Street were the night mails. Again, great progress was made towards streamlining the workings in and out of both Cannon Street and Charing Cross in years just after World War I, when the system of parallel train movements was instituted, to ensure minimum occupation of the track at Borough Market Junction, and a maximum number of trains passing through during the morning and evening suburban rush hours.

But, even so, Cannon Street station itself remained as it had been during the pre-war Continental workings. Some platforms were very long and extended out on to the river bridge, while those on the eastern side of the station, largely used for suburban workings, were relatively short. The electrification scheme planned to come into operation in the summer of 1926 covered no more than suburban workings. A considerable number of Kent Coast residential expresses were run from Cannon Street, morning and evening, for the convenience of City workers, and the remodelling which was planned had to take account of the light-engine workings which would be needed in connection with these long-distance trains from the coast. The most intense studies resulted in a plan for the complete remodelling of the station, in regard to length of platform and track layout as well as signalling. So extensive were the alterations that ultimately the decision was taken to replace the entire layout in the approaches to the station. No piecemeal alterations, no long-protracted stage work would suffice. There was nothing for it but to tear the whole layout up and start afresh. How it was done was a masterpiece of railway engineering, and although it involved the closing of the station for a whole week, the dislocation was relatively small and inconvenience to passengers minimal compared with what would have been necessary had an attempt been made to carry out such changes in stages while the traffic was actually running. In the rest of the area, that is at Borough Market Junction, Metropolitan Junction and Charing Cross, the existing track layouts were maintained.

One of the most important things to be decided in planning the new signalling was what to do with junctions. W. J. Thorrowgood, Signal Engineer of the Southern Railway, favoured using a single colour-light signal with a route indicator above it at every bifurcation. But in actual practice, at that early stage in the development of colour-light signalling this was not found practical. The strength of the light beam from the colour-light signals and the range at which they were to be sighted tended to overpower the indication provided by the route indicators then available, so that in the approach to a junction of this kind the aspect of the signal itself would at first be seen alone and the route discerned only on a closer approach. In the immediate approach to stations, or in the case of platform starting signals where the signals would in any case be seen only at short range, no difficulty was experienced in the use of route indicators. The problem at that stage was governed as much by the prevailing design of route indicator as by the basic principles involved.

In his conception of having a single colour-light signal and a route indicator at every bifurcation, Thorrowgood did not by any means have general support from his fellow signal engineers. In fact when he read a paper on the Southern signalling before the Institution of Railway Signal Engineers in March, 1926, and announced the principle, there was very general opposition to it and general satisfaction that it had not proved practicable in this first installation in the approaches to Charing Cross and Cannon Street. He told how objection had been raised to it by the operating department, and in the discussion following his paper, one speaker after another took up this particular point. The following quotations from the opinions of various eminent signal engineers of the day shows the strength of the opposition to it.

A. F. Bound said that with regard to the route indicator, as he understood it, the author was rather in favour of giving a route indicator on what might be termed running junction signals, and that appeared to be a mistake. There did seem a tendency today to provide route indicators for signals which were really junction signals, and he deplored the practice. The route indicator should be confined to terminal working or intermediate stations of the character of terminals where all speeds were very low. He was absolutely convinced that route indicators were not suitable for high-speed trains.

T. S. Lascelles said he was glad to see that the drivers had asked for splitting signals at the junctions. The English bracket junction signal was the most common-sense signal in the world. It was not correct to say that with it the driver passed a red light. He leaves the red light on one side; the signal says clearly enough 'This way is open but that way is closed'—quite a different thing.

Mr H. H. Dyer of the L.M.S.R. said he heartily agreed that route indicators for junction signalling were a very unsatisfactory arrangement. Then, he went on, stepping was going to be a very difficult matter if they were going to step four-aspect signals. He had come across a very simple and ingenious arrangement to get correct stepping with two-aspect signals. The stepping when the signals were 'on' was not necessary. The two red lights were in line, with the green lens above the red in one case and below in the other, so that if they got twelve-inch spacing between lenses, they always had a twelve-inch stepping. It was difficult to see how to step four-aspect signals.

In the approaches to the larger stations, where track divergencies led to a number of different platforms, route indicators were used from the outset, because speeds in the immediate approaches to stations were necessarily slow. Nevertheless, the form of the actual route indicator was not finalized on the Southern Railway, or elsewhere for that matter, for quite a number of years. At the time the first Southern installations of colour-light signals were brought into service, route indicators in general were only just coming into use and various forms were being experimented with. A fairly common one at that time had been devised on the Lancashire and Yorkshire Railway by Messrs Moore and Berry, and was used in conjunction with electric and electro-pneumatic semaphore signals. It consisted of a large rectangular box in which were contained a number of slides each bearing a letter or platform number. These were normally concealed in one half of the rectangular box and when a route had to be set up the appropriate slide was drawn out into the open half of the rectangular box, and displayed to view. This was quite a simple arrangement mechanically, but large and cumbersome and not suited to signalling with colour-lights.

An indicator embodying the same general principle was designed by the W. R. Sykes Interlocking Signal Company Ltd, for use with colour-light signalling and this, while having a number of stencils concealed from view, was an optical device in that the stencils, as required, were moved between the lamp and a lens. The light of the lamp displayed the figure or letter, illuminating it on a dark background. Indicators of this type were used in the first installations of colour-light signalling on the Southern Railway at Charing Cross, Cannon Street and in the approaches to St Paul's. The figure displayed was rather small, and not too clearly seen at any appreciable distance; and to overcome this disadvantage a totally different form of optical indicator was devised in readiness for future Southern Railway installations of colour-light signalling.

This latter form of indicator used a projector principle, and included a large number of projector units, each containing a stencil of a figure, or letter, which could be projected as required on to a ground glass screen. The figure displayed was twelve inches high. This made a compact unit, as seen from the front, and was capable of ready mounting above a colour-light signal; but to accommodate the projector system inside the case had to be made quite long and it was a cumbersome thing to mount because of this. Nevertheless, from the viewpoint of the indication given to the driver of a train, it was a considerable advance upon the original Sykes indicator, and much more compact than the Moore and Berry type. After a few months of service, however, a disadvantage of the projector type became apparent, in that the glass screen at the front became coated with dust and soot and the indication was seriously affected by the films of dirt that accumulated. Although at that time the inner suburban services of the Southern Railway in the areas concerned had been changed over to electric traction, a considerable number of trains using the termini at Charing Cross and Cannon Street, and more so at London Bridge, were still steam operated. Nevertheless, the optical projector type of indicator was used for a number of important installations on the Southern Railway, and it proved a valuable stepping-stone to a later design, which, to a large extent has been standardized throughout British Railways.

One difficulty anticipated in the early days of colour-light signalling, and especially when four-aspect signals were introduced, was the height at which the uppermost lens of these would be sighted when mounted on gantries or cantilevers spanning the brakes. While the lowest lens of a four-aspect signal would be only a matter of twelve inches above gantry level, the uppermost would be nearly three feet high. It was to meet this difficulty that four-aspect colour-light signals for mounting on gantries were made in the form of a 'cluster' instead of having all four lenses vertically above each other. In the cluster signal the right-hand lens was red and the left-hand one green—each of these aspects being displayed singly. The top and bottom lenses were both yellow, so that in the event of a double-yellow indication being required the configuration of the lenses would be the same as in the ordinary four-aspect signal with all the lenses vertically above each other. Cluster signals were used for all the early installations on the Southern Railway, and they were also used in the first installations of four-aspect colour-light signalling on the London Midland and Scottish Railway at Manchester. After that, however, their use was discontinued.

* * * * * *

It was on the Southern Railway that a very important development in signal control machines took place in the late 1920s. The miniature-lever power interlocking frames installed at Charing Cross, Cannon Street and London Bridge were a direct development of the earliest form of Westinghouse power frame used in the various large installations put into commission before World War I. The interlocking between levers was mechanical, and the only change from the design of pre-war days was that a comprehensive system of visual indications for the colour-light signals and the power-worked points was provided on a display panel immediately behind the levers. The visual illuminated point indications showed 'N' or 'R' as the case might be, while the signal indications showed the actual aspect each particular signal was displaying at the moment, whether 'red', 'single yellow', 'double yellow' or 'green'. The total number of levers in the locking frames at the three largest stations by that time equipped were : Charing Cross—107 levers;

Cannon Street—143; and London Bridge—311. It should be mentioned that prior to the commissioning of the Charing Cross and Cannon Street area some colour-light signalling had also been installed on the former London Chatham and Dover line, with power frames at Blackfriars and St Paul's; but these lay rather outside the continuous line of development that followed the Charing Cross – Cannon Street installations.

The intensity of the work at all three of the large stations was such that the most elaborate provision for alternative route working had to be made, and so that the subsequent development may be better understood a note is necessary on the method of interlocking used. In general terms it is well known that the working of signal levers and point levers is so interlocked that it is mechanically impossible to set up a route that would result in a collision; but the actual method by which this is done can vary according to the nature of the traffic in any particular station. I am not referring here to the details of the mechanical mechanism used for the physical interlocking of the various members, but to the overriding principles by which the scheme of interlocking is prepared. In the early 1920s there were, for example, many different types of mechanical interlocking mechanism used on the full-size mechanical frames, and several varieties of miniature interlocking on power frames. I am not concerned with the details of these. The Southern Railway, in specifying the principle of interlocking required at these very busy terminal stations, laid down the following method:

Each signal, whether for a main-line running movement or for a shunt movement, should be interlocked against any opposing signal, and the route should be checked intermediately according to the position in which the various points were lying. It will perhaps be easier to understand this method if reference is made to a particular case and the approach to Cannon Street Station provides a very good example. At the time the new signalling was installed in 1926, the train service was no more than partly electrified. All the suburban trains were multiple-unit electrics, but the longer-distance residential trains and expresses from coastal resorts were all steam-hauled. These steam-hauled trains were dealt with in the long platforms of the western side of the station, and for each platform road there was a ground shunt signal placed little more than an engine's length from the buffer stops to regulate the movement of light engines after their trains had been drawn out. Each of these shunt signals, or rather the movements they controlled, 'opposed' the home signals, giving entry to the platforms, and therefore the home signals located on a gantry on the viaduct over the Thames, were interlocked against the shunt signals, permitting the movement of a light engine away from the buffer stops. Obviously this would be a conflicting movement and could not be allowed.

The track layout was such that in getting from the up main home signal to No. 1 platform, for example, there were several alternative routes that could be followed covering the negotiation of several pairs of points between the two signals; and therefore the locking between the two signals had to be provided to hold each particular route that was possible. In certain cases there were as many as three possible routes between two signals and one had to provide interlocking such that signal 'A' locked signal 'B' in all those three ways. The locking conditions stipulating the lie of the points for each of the routes, as for example, 'A' must lock 'B' with points 'X'-normal, 'Y'-reversed, and 'Z'-normal; and there might be other routes where 'X' was reversed, 'W' was normal and 'Z' was reversed, and so on.

The resulting mechanical mechanism was complicated. I should explain that in earlier signalling installations the signalling of shunt movements was rarely covered in the interlocking. The routes would be set and all safety measures observed so far as conflicting routes were concerned, but shunt movements were, more often than not, authorized by hand signals from men on the ground, or by megaphone from the signal-box. Such measures would, of course, have been totally inadequate on the Southern Railway, and the signalling of every shunt movement added greatly to the complexity of the interlocking mechanism. Nevertheless, by much very ingenious mechanical design a neat solution was obtained, particularly at Cannon Street where the number of alternative routes was very great. Exactly the same design of mechanism was applied to the very much larger power frame at London Bridge containing 311 levers; and although the apparatus looked just the same as that at Charing Cross and Cannon Street when viewed from the operating room—except of course, that it was much larger—the portion below the floor containing the bulk of the interlocking was such as to demand an overall height below the floor of no less than seven feet six inches.

It will be appreciated that with miniature levers requiring no more than thumb and finger manipulation, and the complete elimination of any necessity for the man to exert a 'pull' on the lever, the mechanisms had not only to be very carefully made, but also erected with precision. The overall length of a locking frame like that at London Bridge involved very long locking bars, in many cases where levers might be interlocked with others thirty or even forty levers away along the frame; and the alignment and levelling during installation had to be well-nigh perfect to get the sweetness which was essential with this kind of apparatus. It is no secret that a lot of difficulty was experienced in the erection of the 311-lever frame at London Bridge; but it was successfully accomplished, and no mechanical adjustments were necessary once the contractors had handed over the frame to the railway company's staff. Nevertheless, the fact that with modern signalling trends locking frames were tending to become so much larger gave rise to certain misgivings as to future progress, and it only needed a request from the Southern Railway to carry out certain alterations to the locking at Cannon Street to trigger off a new line of development.

Cannon Street was perhaps the most intensively locked power frame that has ever been produced, with a vast amount of conditional locking resulting from the locking of signal against signal through every conceivable alternative route. After a year's experience in the working of the station, the operating authorities were convinced that certain alterations to the locking would give improved operation at peak periods in the day. It was estimated to be no more than a fractional improvement, amounting to the saving of an occasional minute in the rush hour; but it was deemed worth while and the re-positioning of one shunt signal and certain alterations to the locking were authorized. That alteration proved a mammoth job in the drawing office, and when it came to install the revised mechanism there was more than a month's work of intricate scheming to alter the already complicated mechanism. The requirements called for even more intense locking in that part of the mechanism where the locking was already thickest. But the work in the drawing office was a minor matter compared to the task of carrying out the change on site.

One cannot alter signalling by a piecemeal process. There has got to be a minimum period when the signalling is disconnected and the change-over is in progress, and the normal time for such change-overs is in the early hours of a Sunday morning when ordinarily the traffic is the lightest in the whole week. Then special arrangements can be made for dealing with the few trains that have to be run, and by Sunday evening the new work can be fully commissioned. The alterations to the locking on the Cannon Street frame, however, were such that far from being capable of being made in a single night it was estimated that the work would take roughly a month of nights, using four locking fitters. As the change, so far as the station itself, could not be made piecemeal, these men had to work for a limited period in the early hours of the morning, fitting new pieces of locking, but before handing the frame back ready for the day's traffic the old had to be put back as it was, so that no change in the circumstances would affect the working in the station. Piece by piece, night after night, the new locking was fitted, and then removed until the date fixed for the final changeover.

I have the most vivid personal memories of this work. I made the drawings, and then on many summer nights I worked with the fitters in the box. We were rarely able to start before 1 a.m., when the Dover Mail had come in, and in the height of the summer we were frequently held up in the small hours, when certain levers were required to admit strawberry specials from Kent. I am afraid we did not think very kindly of strawberries, while we were waiting for levers that we needed for fitting to be freed! Soon after 4 a.m., with the dawn coming up behind Tower Bridge, we had to finish, for the earliest workmen's trains began to arrive. The job of fitting was nevertheless finished on time, and then all the pieces fitted and laid on one side during the previous month of night working were assembled ready for the final change-over. In the early hours of the appointed Sunday morning the bulk of the work was completed and the outdoor change involving the transplanting of a shunt signal was carried out. Cannon Street Station is normally very quiet on a Sunday morning and the checking of the new plant occupied most of the day. But from what I have written

I feel that some appreciation can be made of the magnitude and complexity of the work involved in making this change, to achieve no more than a fractional improvement in traffic facilities.

That change-over, coupled with the difficulties experienced in the installation of the long 311-lever frame at London Bridge, sounded the death knell of mechanical interlocking on the miniature-lever power frames of the Southern Railway. The track circuit and indication locking on these frames was already done electrically, so why not the lever interlocking? Within a year a new type of miniature locking frame had been designed, and the first example installed at North Kent East Junction, between London Bridge and New Cross. This frame, with 83 levers, put into service in 1929, had the levers all in one line; but with mechanical interlocking dispensed with this was no longer essential, and the frames could be built in several sections to suit a more convenient layout of the control room of the signal-box. This latter development is however taking the story somewhat beyond the confines of the present chapter. With the introduction of all-electric interlocking Phase One of power signalling development on the Southern Railway was complete.

CHAPTER VII

The Years of Controversy

With the establishment of colour-light signals as a means of providing greatly improved signalling aspects, a period of acute controversy developed in Great Britain as to the nature of the indicators to be given to the driver. The earliest installations of colour-light signalling on the Southern Railway were based entirely upon the old geographical system of signals. In other words the route that a train was to take was indicated to the driver by a disposition of a group of lights, just as in former days the route was indicated by the configuration of a group of semaphore arms. The actual disposition presented to the driver was in the process of being greatly simplified by the use of route indicators instead of a multiplicity of lights; though at junction locations where fast running was made, nothing in colour-light signalling had yet been introduced to supersede a geographical arrangement of the lights. Notwithstanding the fact that the period commencing at the year 1930 was one of very serious trade depression, considerable enterprise was being shown by all the main-line railways in Great Britain towards the accelerating of express train services, and on certain routes the speeds in everyday running were higher than anything previously attained regularly. The need to inform drivers without any possible doubt of the state of the line ahead was, therefore, of increased importance.

A considerable body of opinion among signal engineers held the view that it was more important to advise a driver of the speed at which he should travel, rather than give him an indication of the geographical course his train was to take. It was argued that if signals were installed giving indications that meant travel at medium speed, and travel at low speed, in addition to those

79

indicating 'unlimited speed' and 'stop', the requirements of modern traffic would be better satisfied than by a system of signalling which told the driver that he was going to cross over from one set of tracks to another, or that he was going to travel down a branch line. In these two latter cases it was accepted that the man himself would be familiar with his route, and would know when a cross-over movement or a turn-out would necessitate reduction of speed to limits specified in the working timetable.

Both these arguments had a good deal to be said for them. Opponents of the principle of speed signalling argued that it would be possible to send a train on to an entirely wrong route, through a signalman's error. The driver would be told the speed he had to travel, and when he reached a junction, having made the necessary reduction of speed, he might find himself switched onto a line that would not take him to his scheduled destination. In such a case a stop would be called for. The fireman would have to be sent to the signal-box to explain matters, and the subsequent reversal would inevitably result in some delay, not only of the train in question, but very likely to others. Furthermore, it was argued that a driver in such circumstances might imagine that he was being diverted for a specific purpose and might continue for some distance until the error was discovered; whereupon the delay would be even more severe. Opponents of the long-established geographical signalling argued that although the signals indicated quite clearly to a driver the route he had to take, he might in a moment of forgetfulness misjudge his speed and take the diverging route at such a speed as to be very unsafe and uncomfortable, if it did not in effect lead to an actual derailment.

In semaphore signalling practice, where divergencies that involved considerable reduction in speed were to take place, various devices were used to remind the driver of the impending turn-out. If distant signals were provided it was usual not to lower the distant at all for a sharp diverging move, or alternatively to provide distant arms permanently fixed in the warning position. Where only one distant signal arm was provided in the approach to a turn-out this would not be lowered at all for the diverging moment, and the home signal would be lowered to indicate the turn-out only when the signalman saw for himself that the approaching train had slowed down.

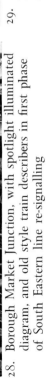

ANICAL
FRAMES
IN
COLOUR-
LIGHT
TERRI-
TORY

28. Borough Market Junction, with spotlight illuminated diagram, and old style train describers in first phase of South Eastern line re-signalling

29. Local signal-box at Smeafield—Newcastle – Berwick main line, for level-crossing gate control and emergency cross-over. Note miniature electrical equipment in cabin to left.

PADDINGTON
ARRIVAL
BOX

30. A fine example of the
G.R.S. type of locking
frame, with slide levers
and dynamic indication

Euston No. 2 just prior to its replacement in 1952

FAMOUS SIGNAL-BOXES

Glasgow Central, installed in 1908, containing the largest British power frame ever built—374 levers

33. Cannon Street, Southern Railway, installed in 1926

CHANGES IN SIGNAL-BOX DECOR

34. Coventry, London Midland Region, British Railways, 1962, showing the t⟩
regulator's desk, and the lady train announcer

With colour-light signalling an approach control by track circuit was in certain cases included in the signalling of the diverging movement, delaying the clearance of the junction aspect until the train had approached within a specified distance. With four-aspect signalling one could have, sequentially, 'double yellow', 'single yellow', and then a delayed clearance of the final signal at the immediate approach of the train. Those who argued for the retention of the geographical system of signalling, felt that it was of the utmost importance to insist upon the continuance of the long-cherished British principle of operation that the driver should possess a thorough knowledge of the road. This had been established in days when the night indication of the distant signals was exactly the same as that of the stop signals, and only the driver's intimate knowledge of the road would enable him to recognize the distant signals as he was approaching the various locations, and to know which reds he could pass, and at which he was compelled to stop.

As a young engineer I used to listen with intense interest to the discussions that took place inside my own firm and at meetings of the Institution of Railway Signal Engineers, particularly because of my own interest in locomotive running and work on the footplate. It seemed to me then that all the arguments about the logic or otherwise of signal aspects, the claims and counter-claims of speed *versus* geographical signalling, were quite secondary, and the main thing was to provide good visibility above all other considerations. Enginemen welcomed with open arms the introduction of colour-light signalling. Many years later I remember very vividly discussing certain points of signal aspects with a group of enginemen and running inspectors and at one stage in our discussions one of my friends rather brushed aside the argument of signal aspects, saying: 'We know our road and know what the signals mean, but can you please give us something we can *see*.' Not long after this particular talk I happened to be riding with one of these men on a late evening train out of London on a route that had colour-light signals only for the first dozen miles. As we approached the end of the colour-light area the driver shouted across to me: 'Now for the candles!'

Nevertheless the principle of speed signalling had some very powerful advocates in the early 1930s. Foremost among these was

A. F. Bound, who by this time was Signal Engineer of the London Midland and Scottish Railway. In earlier years he had been one of the strongest advocates of signalling progress and when Signal Engineer of the Great Central Railway had rather shocked some of his more conservative contemporaries on other railways by the very advanced nature of his views. It was, however, one thing for the signal engineer of one of the pre-grouping companies, and one moreover that because of its state of continual financial stringency had little money to spend on new developments, to be advocating radical changes in British signalling practice; it was quite another for the signal engineer of the largest and most extensive of the 'Big Four' of grouping days to be advocating great changes. Yet here, at a meeting of the Institution of Railway Signal Engineers in March 1932, was the one-time *enfant terrible* of the Great Central at it again. His hearers could not think otherwise than that this paper was a forecast of things to come on the L.M.S.R. And yet, while Bound had then a vastly greater canvas on which to work, the circumstances were not entirely parallel. On the L.M.S.R., the Traffic Department was in most respects omnipotent where matters of train working were concerned. They even dictated to the Chief Mechanical Engineer on one memorable occasion how many cylinders he should use in the largest express passenger locomotives! The Signal Engineer could not do otherwise than signal the line as the Traffic Department wished.

Even so, Bound was an independent senior officer, reporting direct to one of the Vice-Presidents of the railway, and in status he was certainly the equal of the Chief Operating Manager and the Chief Mechanical Engineer. In such a position his advice must certainly have been given the most serious consideration, and the outcome of his powerful advocacy of speed signalling—as distinct from geographical or route signalling—was a notable installation of colour-light signals at Mirfield. This important junction lies on the main line of the former Lancashire and Yorkshire Railway from Manchester to Wakefield and York. At Mirfield the L.&Y.R. line is intersected for a short distance by the rival L.&N.W. line from Manchester to Leeds. The L.&Y. main line has quadrupled track throughout, and the L.N.W. line, coming in from Huddersfield and afterwards turning north towards Dewsbury and Morley, also carries a heavy traffic. On both sides of Mirfield station there are comprehensive cross-over roads, permitting of various alternative routes through the station for trains taking the main L.&Y.R. line and by the intersecting L.N.W. line. It was an ideal location for an experiment in speed signalling. L.&Y.R. trains running through on the main lines could be run at maximum speed if not stopping at Mirfield station; but to fit in with other traffic it might be necessary to involve cross-over movements from fast to slow lines and vice versa. The intersecting L.&N.W. trains had in any case to reduce speed in taking the junctions to both east and west of Mirfield, and they also were sometimes involved in cross-over movements on the quadruple-track line of the L.&Y.R. during the few miles that they were using it.

The system installed made use of the searchlight type of colour-light signal, which was ideal for the particular arrangements. Instead of having the signal units arranged geographically, so that the left-hand signal cleared meant one was taking the left-hand route, and the right-hand one vice versa, the signal units were displayed vertically, the majority of locations having three units, one above the other. The signalling was three-aspect in character, but the lowermost of the three units was a marker light which normally remained permanently at red, to indicate that the system was one of speed signalling. At a simple junction the uppermost unit related to the straight road and the central one to the divergence, whether it was to the right or to the left. If the line was clear to proceed at unlimited speed on the straight road, the lights reading from top to bottom were green, red, red. If however the straight line ahead was clear only up to the next signal, the uppermost unit would show yellow to indicate, as in ordinary three-aspect signalling, that the next location ahead was displaying red. If on the other hand the divergence had got to be taken the middle unit was used, and even though a reduction of speed was required for the divergence the lights would read 'red', 'green', 'red' from top to bottom, if the line ahead was clear. If it was clear only up to the next signal the lights would read 'red', 'yellow', 'red'. It was the vertical disposition of the lights that indicated speed to the driver. With green uppermost he could travel at unlimited speed. With red over green he was required to travel at medium speed because of the divergence.

There were very strong advocates for speed signalling in other

83

countries, notably the USA and Australia, and until the installation at Mirfield was put in those British engineers who favoured speed signalling could point only to installations abroad, rather than anything at home which had provided some practical experience. Mirfield was therefore a milestone, because it not only set up a British example of speed signalling on the latest principles advocated abroad and enthusiastically followed by Bound himself, but it provided equally an 'Aunt Sally' on which all opponents of the idea could test their skill. More than thirty years later Mirfield is still operating as Bound designed it; and it remains a milestone, but a completely negative one. What discussions went on within the inner councils of the L.M.S.R. we are not to know, and the fact that it was not repeated could well be taken as an admission of failure. At the same time, however, signalling policy on the L.M.S.R. throughout the 1930s seemed to lie dormant. Apart from Mirfield no major new works were undertaken, and it seemed that practice continued to be built round the time-honoured mechanical signalling reinforced by track circuit control, starting signal control, and feelers towards the adoption of a new system of Automatic Train Control.

Mirfield was a pointer in another direction. One would have thought that the compact area, with the station at the centre and the various outlying junction of main routes lying to east and west, would have been ideal for a single unified power interlocking with an illuminated diagram covering the whole area and worked from one signal-box. Instead, however, mechanical working was retained, and the colour-light signals were operated by circuit controllers from the levers of the mechanical locking frames. Individual signal-boxes were retained for all the outlying junctions. Mirfield was indeed an experiment in signal indications only, without any attempt at concentration of control. This practice can be traced through the few new works that were undertaken on the L.M.S.R. during the period 1932-9. Marginal improvements in the signalling were certainly made on an extensive scale, but these were little more than of a routine nature and not the kind of programme that one would have expected from an engineer of Bound's personality. One is drawn inevitably to the conclusion that the controversial practice he received authority to try out at Mirfield was not generally to the liking of the Operating Department and in consequence not repeated. While a great deal was done to improve running conditions on the L.M.S.R. system by the replacement of semaphore distant signals by colour-lights, and longer spacing of distant signals to provide increased braking distance for higher speeds, so far as the evolution of signalling practice in general was concerned the period that began with such a flourish, and promise of much controversy, largely ended in stagnation.

Speed signalling had another enthusiastic advocate in G. H. Crook, Assistant Signal Engineer of the Great Western Railway. He spoke of it frequently in discussion at the Institution of Railway Signal Engineers and developed his idea in some interesting papers. But his views found no response at all on his own railway. The Great Western was indeed one of the most conservative of all main-line companies during the grouping era, and its policy regarding the installation of colour-light signals is discussed at some length in a later chapter. So far as speed signalling in Great Britain was concerned the practice was confined to Mirfield.

CHAPTER VIII

Tattersall, the Man of Vision

The scene now moved to the North Eastern Area of the L.N.E.R., where Arthur Ewart Tattersall had been appointed Signal and Telegraph Engineer in 1928. In that post he was not an independent officer, being responsible to 'The Engineer'—that was the chief civil engineer of the Area, who embraced signalling in his overall command. This was a continuance of a practice that was usual on most British railways. At the time of grouping it was only on the Great Western that the signal engineer held 'chief officer' status. Even on the L.M.S.R., at the start of the grouping era, the responsibility for signalling was divisionalized, until Bound's appointment. Nevertheless, although he had not enjoyed the highest status, Tattersall had already made an indelible mark on signalling history, even before he went to York in 1928. As the Signalling and Electrical Assistant to the Engineer of the Metropolitan Railway from 1907 to 1920, he completely modernized the signalling throughout the electrified area of that railway, carrying out the notable development of dispensing with facing-point lockbars in track-circuited areas. In 1921 he went to the Great Northern and, after grouping, from 1924 was assistant to Bound, who was then Signal Engineer of the Southern Area of the L.N.E.R.

At York he became associated with that great railway personality John Miller, who was 'The Engineer'. The responsibility of the civil engineer for signalling dates from the earliest days of railway. The famous disc and crossbar signals used on the Great Western were designed by Brunel and signals, being fixed structures alongside the line, were naturally maintained, in early days, by 'The Engineer'. As the art and science of signalling developed, the relations between the Engineer and his assistant responsible for signalling were not always of the happiest. Things were not always so wholeheartedly co-operative as they were on the London and South Western for example, when A. W. Szlumper was London Divisional Engineer, and the great re-signalling of Waterloo Station took place in the early 1900s. But at York from 1928 onwards the partnership of Miller and Tattersall was extremely fruitful.

They were not easy days for men of boundless enterprise and initiative. The London and North Eastern Railway, more perhaps than any other of the 'Big Four' companies of grouping days, was hit very hard by the economic slump. At the time of grouping, in 1923, some of its constituents were prosperous and profitable to their shareholders. One indeed, the North Eastern, was one of the richest lines in the country. But the grouping scheme also placed in the L.N.E.R. fold one fairly large concern, with high capital investment, that had scarcely paid its ordinary shareholders any dividend at all for the past twenty-five years; and some of the Scottish constituents were not exactly prosperous. So, with the utmost wisdom, the management of the L.N.E.R. took a very tight hold on the purse-strings. The budgets of all departments were cut to the closest limits commensurate with the maintenance of the plant in first-class order, and little cash was made available for schemes of capital investment.

Fortunately for the North Eastern Area, John Miller was one of those men who are completely undeterred by adverse circumstances, and who in fact take such circumstances as a challenge. The North Eastern Area of the L.N.E.R. served districts that were among the most grievously hit by chronic unemployment, on Tyne and Teesside, and in the great shipyards of Jarrow and Wallsend. In these depressing conditions Miller set out to give every man on his strength a new sense of pride in the job. He argued that if everything was neat and tidy, and kept looking smart, the cost of maintenance could well be less than if things were allowed to slide 'because there was no money'. The lineside was tidied up from end to end. Even the smallest huts received attention, and at some of the larger stations the co-operation of the Newcastle firm of seedsmen, Finney's, was secured to plant ornamental lawns in the triangular spaces at junctions and elsewhere between tracks. In return for a small and quite unobtrusive advertisement on each plot, Miller got beautifully kept lawns, for nothing:

87

pre-cast concrete edgings were added, and these latter became familiar in edging the ballast on open line. His premise was amply fulfilled, and this astonishing 'face-lift' to all important lines of the North Eastern Area was achieved comfortably *within* his somewhat meagre budget allowance. In fact there was sufficient surplus for him to build and equip a splendid gymnasium for the men at York!

Into this inspiriting atmosphere came Tattersall. While Miller was a human dynamo, a shrewd judge of character and a magnificent leader of men, Tattersall was a man of vision. He realized, no more clearly perhaps than some of his more forward-thinking colleagues on other railways, that the rapid development of signalling techniques was opening up new vistas of railway operating control. He declared that technically there would soon be no limit to the physical area that could be controlled from one signal-box, and he was fortunate in having beside him in York railwaymen of the stature of John Miller and C. M. Jenkin-Jones, who were prepared to allow him to begin to develop his ideas. The heart of any control system is the control centre itself, and Tattersall began to look forward to the time when the signal-box and the control-room would be combined. All the same, despite the introduction of all-electric interlocking, and the possibility of building locking frames in a series of facets instead of one long line of levers, a really large interlocking with over 300 miniature levers was a rather unwieldy instrument when it came to centralized supervision.

Having abolished mechanical interlocking, the next stage was to abolish the positive interlock altogether and to use instead circuit interlocking. The various conditions that arise from the lie of points, aspect of signals and so on could be simulated by relays, and the movement of a pair of points or the clearing of a signal initiated by the actuation of a thumb-switch. Though this switch was not interlocked in the physical sense, if it was moved, and the conditions were incorrect or unsafe, the signal or pair of points concerned would not operate. The substitution of thumb-switches for miniature interlocked levers would make possible a great reduction in the size of the control instrument, and constitute a major step towards Tattersall's vision of the large signal-boxes and the traffic control centres being combined. Very wisely, his first practical application of this new concept was on a minor scale, at a small interlocking with colour-light signals, controlling the approaches to the swing-bridge over the River Ouse near Goole. It was not widely publicized, and it attracted little attention; but it provided Tattersall and his staff with invaluable experience, enabling them to go ahead in confidence on the next, and much more spectacular stage.

In the early 1930s, under an arrangement of loans and guarantees from the Government, all the British railways undertook major works for the relief of unemployment, and under this arrangement the North Eastern Area of the L.N.E.R. carried out a scheme of main-line widening between York and Northallerton. Extra running lines were laid in for long stretches of this almost level thirty-mile racing ground, in some instances providing three, and in others four tracks. Colour-light signals of the searchlight type were installed throughout and comprehensive arrangements were made for cross-over movements to and from the main and relief lines, in both the down and up directions. The signals were spaced with mathematical precision, to provide uniform headway between trains, and the majority normally worked as automatics. There were some small intermediate interlockings, but the point of major interest was Thirsk. The area controlled by the new signal-box there was not extensive, although a considerable number of freight, shunting, and cross-over movements had to be provided for, in addition to the continual passage of through express passenger trains travelling generally at speeds of about 75 m.p.h. It was at this interlocking that Tattersall installed a relay circuit system, but included in it complete route control, in which the turning of one thumb-switch set up an entire route. All the points concerned, sometimes for a complicated movement right across the whole area, responded—if the electric interlocking was free—to the turning of one switch by the signalman.

The equipment of the whole line between York and Northallerton was exceptionally interesting, because while Thirsk was the only complete route relay interlocking with power operation throughout, a number of other signal-boxes were equipped on the electro-mechanical principle using keys for the signals, and having the majority of the points operated by mechanical rodding. As on the Thirsk panel the interlocking between signals and points was electrical. Statistics of the complete installation were:

89

Distance from York (miles)	Signal-box	System of interlocking	Route keys	Signal keys	Point keys	Mech. point levers
5·5	Beningborough	Elec-Mech.	—	11	2	15
9·7	Tollerton	Elec-Mech.	—	9	2	15
11·2	Alne	Elec-Mech.	—	8	1	20
	Raskelf	Elec-Mech.	—	3	—	12
	Pilmoor	Elec-Mech.	—	4	—	31
	Sessay Wood Junction	Elec-Mech.	—	12	4	13
22·5	Thirsk	All-electric route system	135	—	34	—
26·5	Otterington	Elec-Mech.	—	8	1	18

The development of relay, or circuit interlocking, as distinct from the positive physical interlocking of levers so long traditional of British railway practice, was received with very mixed feelings by many signal engineers. The mere fact that an operating key could be turned when the signal or pair of points was in fact 'locked', ran counter to all established ideas, and very numerous in those early days were the prophets of woe! The actual position of the levers in a locking frame, whether full-sized or the miniature levers of a power frame, did provide a visual picture of the state of a yard, so far as the point setting was concerned, whereas in the new system it was argued that a signalman could move a key, to shift a pair of points, and if they did not move the key could still be left temporarily not corresponding with the actual lie of the points. A complete system of indication lights was provided, but many felt that it would take time before signalmen came to rely on these in the same way as they had previously done with the actual positions of the levers.

Quite apart from the principle of relay interlocking, Tattersall had not moved far, on the York – Northallerton installation, towards his aim of a much more concentrated control. The various small interlockings enumerated in the foregoing table retained the previous box-to-box method of working. Each reported to York traffic control, and it was there rather than in a major signal-box that co-ordination of working was initiated. For all that, however, Tattersall, to use modern popular jargon, had achieved a major 'break-through' at Thirsk, and its success paved the way for some much more striking developments in a few years time. The extent to which the area of the control-room could be reduced was strikingly demonstrated. To operate the same area in the old style would have required a miniature-lever frame of 300 levers, and the respective floor areas of the control-rooms would have been:

    (a) With a power frame   1,300 sq. ft.

    (b) With the panel actually installed   300 sq. ft.

The trend towards miniaturization had certainly begun at Thirsk.

It was on the main line of the North Eastern Area of the L.N.E.R. that the vexed problem of long-range junction indication was largely solved. In an earlier chapter dealing with the adaptation of the standard mechanical splitting signals to colour-light practice, it will be recalled that when W. J. Thorrowgood read his paper on multi-aspect colour-light signals, several speakers expressed their gratification that the indications displayed in semaphore signalling practice were being retained in colour-light areas. In the comparatively confined areas in the Southern Railway suburban systems, in the immediate approaches to Charing Cross, Cannon Street and London Bridge, and in the subsequent use of the same system of signalling at the Victoria and Exchange stations in Manchester on the London Midland and Scottish Railway, the splitting principle with the signal for the more important of two routes raised above the other proved quite adequate. It was also used on the York – Northallerton section when that line was first put into commission in 1933, though in the later case searchlight signals were used, as distinct from multi-aspect signals on the L.M.S.R. As previously indicated, the York – Northallerton section, with its lengthy stretches of quadruple and three-line track, included many cross-overs where trains could be switched from one set of tracks to another as occasions demanded, and these junction locations were originally all equipped with splitting signals, stepped as previously.

The difference on the York – Northallerton section was that many of the signals could be sighted over very long distances. The country through which the line runs is for the most part level, and quite open, and the railway itself includes many long stretches of absolutely straight track. In consequence some of the junction locations could be sighted from as much as two miles away or even more. At one time Tattersall proposed to effect economy in signal lighting and life of lamps by use of a system of approach lighting, whereby signals were only lighted on the approach of a train. This lighting up, of course, took place in plenty of time for the driver to observe the 'caution' indication if such were given, and to act upon it; but the number of trains using the section was so great that the economies derived from approach lighting were relatively small, having regard to the additional equipment required to provide the facility. Most of the signals were continuously lighted, and at such long range the splitting principle with stepped aspects was not satisfactory. At night in particular, as I observed several times from the footplate, the first sight one would get of a junction signal would be an indistinct haze of white light. As one drew nearer this would be resolved into a green light for the main line and a red light for the turn-out; but unless drivers knew the road very thoroughly such aspects could be misleading, and it was not until one approached near enough for the haze of white to be resolved that one could tell whether the road was set for the straight or for the turn-out.

Tattersall therefore set out to provide a distinctive form of junction indicator that could be used with no more than a single unit for each particular location. He devised a direction indicator, the original form of which consisted of a series of neon tubes radiating from the single-lens unit of the searchlight signal covering the junction. If the road was set for the straight line ahead, the tube pointing vertically upwards was illuminated. If the road was set for a single turn-out to the left a tube pointing diagonally to the left was illuminated, while the second and sharper turn-out to the left was indicated by a neon tube pointing horizontally to the left. The principle was very simple and immediately successful, though the first installation of such an indicator at Thirsk, using a red neon tube, involved the same confusion of aspects, seen from a distance, as had prevailed with the splitting colour-light signal with stepped aspects, because the neon tubes used were red.

I shall always remember the first time I encountered this pioneer junction indicator in the North Eastern Area. It was in the southern approaches to Thirsk, and I was riding at night on one of the Gresley 'A1' Pacifics. We were running on a very clear, frosty, and moonlit night, travelling at between 65 and 70 m.p.h. all the way, and by the time we were approaching Thirsk I had grown used to the haze of white light which heralded our approach to each of the junction signals. Approaching Thirsk we had just the same effect, yet as we drew near the haze resolved itself into the red neon tube, pointing vertically upwards from the junction signal, which was showing green. After that first experiment a row of five white lights was substituted for the neon tube and this was the form finally standardized in the North Eastern Area of the L.N.E.R. Almost simultaneously the junction indicator was adopted as standard on the Southern Railway, where the introduction of colour-light signals on the former London and South Western line between Waterloo and Hampton Court Junction posed exactly the same problem in sighting that had been experienced on the long straight stretches of the L.N.E.R. between York and Northallerton. On the Southern however the indicator had only three white lights in a row as distinct from five on the L.N.E.R. Both companies in their standardized form had no junction indication for the straight line ahead. The white lights, inclined one way or the other, were only displayed when there was to be a divergence to right or left of the main line.

CHAPTER IX

Two Standard Systems: Southern and Great Western

A general survey of British signalling developments in the 1930s would show the widest possible divergencies in practice between the four main-line companies. All complied, of course, with the basic requirements of the Ministry of Transport, and the code of signal aspects was the same; but the philosophy guiding the principles of control were entirely diverse. In the two previous chapters extended reference has been made to work on the L.M.S.R. and L.N.E.R.: innovation followed by stagnation in the one case, and steady and sustained evolution in the other. We have now to consider events on the Southern and on the Great Western. The earlier developments in colour-light signalling practice on the Southern have already been described in some detail, and the principles laid down by Thorrowgood, and developed by Col. G. L. Hall and W. Challis, were well established by the beginning of the 1930s. In signal-box control the substitution of the new-type locking frame with all-electric lever interlocking was little more than incidental, so far as the overall system was concerned — great though the benefits were in signal-box design and maintenance.

The most important changes, so far as the indications given to the driver were concerned, related to the form of route indicators and subsidiary signals. These changes were manifest at the time of the resignalling of Waterloo and its approach lines, but the development of Southern signalling had in the meantime been strikingly demonstrated at the time of the electrification of the Brighton line, which was completed during the year 1932. At the time of this very important development in Southern Railway operating, the London area had been equipped with colour-light signalling only between London Bridge and New Cross; the alternative route for Brighton traffic out of London, from Victoria, remained as previously, with semaphore signals and Sykes 'lock and block'. The same form of signalling remained between New Cross and the converging junction of the two routes at East Croydon. 'Lock and block' working remained over the very densely trafficked section between East Croydon and Coulsdon, but the remaining part of the line throughout to Brighton, including Brighton itself, was equipped continuously with colour-light signalling.

Throughout this extensive work the signals units, the route indications, and the subsidiary signals were of the same type as employed at London Bridge; but the signalling itself, taking the line as a whole, was an excellent example of the improved methods of working possible with the new apparatus. In the thirty-six miles between Coulsdon and Brighton no fewer than twenty-four signal-boxes, containing between them 1,093 levers, were totally abolished. Nine boxes having an aggregate of 324 levers were retained, but were normally switched out and used only in emergency. For the rest of the line there were seven signal-boxes with mechanical frames, having a total of 417 levers, and at the Brighton terminus there was a new all-electric interlocking with a frame of 225 levers. Thus in normal working only eight signal-boxes were required to work thirty-six miles of one of the busiest double-tracked main lines to be found anywhere in the country.

Except at Brighton itself, all the locking frames were of the full-sized mechanical lever type. The colour-light signals were operated by circuit-breakers attached to the tails of the levers, and most of the points were worked mechanically through rodding; only those pairs lying beyond the limit of mechanical operation were power-worked. It was a very simple and economical scheme and, in contrast to the developments that were taking place contemporaneously in the North Eastern Area of the L.N.E.R., all the interlocking between levers was mechanical. In most of the signal-boxes new locking frames were installed, and considerable ingenuity was shown in mounting these in the same operating room, while the existing frame was still in service. During the transition period conditions were inclined to be cramped for the men; but the high cost of providing new signal-box structures was avoided by this clever procedure. The older locking frames were mostly of the historic Saxby and Farmer 'rocker and grid' type, and

95

the replacements were of the Saxby catch-handle-locking pattern, first introduced in 1914 and later developed in a slightly modified version introduced in 1924.

In referring to the installation of the new locking frames in the old signal-boxes I have opened up the subject of 'change-overs' in general. The traditional method of carrying out a signal change-over was always to obtain absolute possession of the line, so far as the working of signals was concerned, at a weekend, usually commencing shortly before midnight on Saturday and often continuing throughout Sunday. During such change-over periods a certain amount of re-routing of trains had to be arranged in order to give the signal department an opportunity to disconnect and reconnect point connections, while throughout the change-over period the area in question was subject to hand signalling only—none of the fixed signals, either old or new, being in service. It was often a lengthy process and I have personally participated in openings that continued for twenty-four hours and more. On a line like Brighton such protracted occupation would have been intolerable. The line carries a heavy traffic on Sundays in the form of excursions and other regular trains to the seaside, and to have even the briefest 'possession' would lead to delays, causing inconvenience to the public and loss of good-will. The signal department of the Southern Railway therefore devised and perfected special techniques for ensuring the change-over of signalling in the quickest possible time.

It was, of course, a relatively simple matter to connect up the colour-light signals to the circuit-breakers on the new locking frames, and to have the track circuits tested out beforehand. All the track circuits could be brought into operation, and in the case of points, where these were being changed over from mechanical working to power, these were also coupled up, brought into service and operated from temporary circuit controllers attached to the old locking frames. The new circuits were also wired in and tested, and on the opening night all that had to be done in many cases was to take the fuses out of one circuit and insert those in another. The saving in time by this well-planned and carefully practised method was really quite phenomenal. The whole line between Coulsdon and Brighton was brought into service in four stages, without any interruption to traffic, as follows:

35.
Cannon Street home
signals, with early form
of optical route indicator,
1926

36.
Pre-cast concrete cantilever
structures, in re-signalling
at Bricklayers Arms
Junction, 1950

37.
'Cluster' type four-aspe
signals near London
Bridge, Southern Railw

38.
Signals at Carlisle marshalling
yard, with wire cages to
protect maintenance men from
contact with overhead traction
wires, when installed

THE CONTROL ROOM AT YORK

39. At the time of its installation, in 1951, the largest route relay interlocking in the world

41. Installation work on the L.M.R. electrified line at

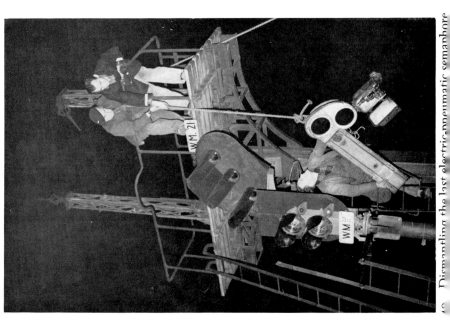

42. Dismantling the last electric-pneumatic semaphore

SIGNAL-
LING
CHANGE-
OVERS

Section	Locality	Mileage involved	Time of change-overs
1	Coulsdon and Balcombe	—	6 hrs.
2	Balcombe to Copyhold Junction	—	¼ hr. on each line
3	Haywards Heath and Preston	—	1 hr.
4	Brighton Station.	—	6½ hrs.

The Southern Railway signalling department became even more 'slick' as time went on and in 1939, when the new signalling at Victoria was brought into operation, the complete change-over on the Brighton side of the station, including the commissioning of a new 225-lever frame, was completed in about forty minutes.

Even as early in the signalling modernization programme on the Southern Region as the work on the Brighton line, in 1932, practices were becoming standardized. More and more staff were becoming familiar with the new equipment and the individual techniques, and this degree of standardization was paying rich dividends in the freedom from trouble experienced when each new installation was brought into service, and in the complete absence of any interruption to traffic through the inexperience of installation staff or complications which signalmen themselves had got to learn. With the power boxes the fact that so much of the work was entirely complete before the opening, and all the track circuits were working, enabled signalmen when nominally off duty to familiarize themselves with the new equipment, watching the progress of the trains on the illuminated diagram and 'going through the motions' of signalling, even though their lever pulling did not at that time actuate any of the new signals or electric point machines. When they came to take over the new boxes they were already familiar with the equipment.

So far as the signal department was concerned, the very big re-signalling scheme on the former London and South Western line covering the approaches to Waterloo from as far out as Hampton Court Junction, and the re-signalling of Waterloo itself, was 'just another job'! The sheer size of the locking frame itself at Waterloo, with its total of 334 levers, raised some problems in connection with the form the illuminated diagrams should take and the final layout of the signal-box was not determined until a number of experimental mock-ups had been examined. But so far as the signalling itself was concerned, the principal changes in the

G

approaches to Waterloo were the first use of the junction indicators, designed on similar lines to those developed in the North Eastern Area of the L.N.E.R., and referred to in the previous chapter; the use of the theatre-sign type of indicator for short-range indications, such as platform starters; and the abandonment of colour-light signals for all subsidiary movements. The use of a miniature form of colour-light signal for shunting, calling-on or backing movements had never been really satisfactory and attempts had been made to differentiate between main and subsidiary signals by use of considerably smaller lenses and less bright indications; but these had the disadvantage of showing up poorly in sunshine and on one occasion a driver not entirely familiar with the signalling in the London area ignored the shunt signal on the ground just below his engine, saw a green light ahead of him and drew out, to collide with another train at London Bridge.

A sustained attempt was made for some years to try and secure a satisfactory compromise between the conflicting demands of a signal that should be of a size roughly distinguishable from a main-line signal, and distinguishable also in the power of the light beam, and which would yet provide something that could be seen at all angles and in broad daylight. At Waterloo and on the approach lines a totally different solution was reached by use of electrically-operated disc signals having an enamelled disc, white with a red band, which would be very clearly visible and unmistakable by day. There was, of course, nothing new in using disc signals for subsidiary purposes, but previously the night indication had been given by lights showing through small roundels in the disc. The novelty on the Southern was that the discs were floodlighted at night. The drivers themselves saw exactly the same indications by day and by night, and what they saw was always something that was quite distinct from the main running signals, which were of course long-range colour-lights. These electrically-worked floodlighted disc signals were used both for ground shunts and for subsidiaries associated with the main running signals. At Waterloo itself the platform starting signals each consisted of a group of three units: the main colour-light; a theatre-sign indicator to tell the driver which running line he would travel on; and a floodlighted subsidiary signal which was cleared to allow a shunting movement.

The experience gained in these earlier schemes was shown in the work carried out during the last five years before World War II. The electrification of the Portsmouth Direct line called for varying degrees of re-signalling. There was not a steady flow of traffic, such as passed over the Brighton main line. The express train service was based upon the periodic sailings from Portsmouth Harbour to the Isle of Wight, and provision had to be made for the working of express trains in two or more portions, running four or five minutes apart; after such a series there might be an interval of twenty minutes or so. The gradients over the greater part of the route are severe and, in order to preserve a uniformly close headway between successive trains, intermediate colour-light signals were provided on steep inclines where, even with electric traction, speed dropped considerably below the average for the whole run. Much the same conditions existed in the Mid-Sussex, or Portsmouth No. 2 Scheme, on the awkwardly graded section between Dorking and Horsham.

The coastal termini, too, presented quite a different problem in signalling from that of great stations in the London area, such as Waterloo and Cannon Street. During the summer, Portsmouth Harbour was then handling a volume of traffic that was quite heavy in relation to its limited platform accommodation, but conditions at Bognor Regis and Littlehampton were less exacting. The new signalling work in the latter cases was occasioned largely on account of the lengthening of platforms to berth twelve-car electric trains and by the simplifying of track layouts made possible by the elimination of light-engine movements. At the larger intermediate junctions a variety of operating conditions might exist in one location. At Havant, for example, in addition to the junction of two main routes from London to Portsmouth, two busy level-crossings were controlled, and the Hayling Island shuttle service was normally operated with no physical connection to the main line.

With the exception of Brighton Central station, where the traffic both in nature and volume resembles that of a London terminus, there was by the end of 1939 only one complete power scheme, with all-electric locking frame, outside the London area; that was at Woking, and it was designed similarly to those at Clapham Junction, West London Junction, and the approach lines to Waterloo. At all other locations a mechanical locking frame was used and electric power employed for the actuation of only those functions that could not be satisfactorily controlled manually. The signals, for example, were generally mechanical upper-quadrant semaphores, but at certain key points such as Havant, Horsham, Dorking and Guildford traffic considerations warranted the use of three-indication or four-indication signals, and here of course long-range day colour-light signals were installed. But even in such cases as many of the shunt signals as possible were manually worked; those were of the disc type, floodlit at night at those interlockings where colour-lights are used for the running signals. Those shunt signals which were situated some distance from the signal-box, as for example at the south end of Horsham station, were operated by electric solenoids. At stations where semaphore signals were used throughout, the distants were operated by electric signal machines. Thus almost every interlocking was a judicious combination of power and mechanical signalling. The same applied to the operation of points; electric machines were used only for those layouts which were too far from the signal-box for manual control.

At all interlockings, whether colour-light or semaphore signals were used, or whether the points were power- or rod-worked, a very complete scheme of track and indication locking was applied to all levers of the frame. All running lines were track-circuited through the area controlled by the signal-box and, by fitting the levers in the frame with electric lever locks and multi-contact circuit controllers driven off the lever tails, all the additional protection of a full-power interlocking was obtained.

The use of splitting signals for junctions, in the case of both diverging lines and the approaches to terminal stations, could, by 1939, be considered obsolete on the Southern Railway. In the area under consideration there were, of course, a number of instances where the existing semaphores had not yet been replaced; but for all new work, route indicators were being installed. At terminal stations, where it was necessary to advise the motorman of the platform at which he would arrive, route indicators of the multiple-lamp or theatre-sign type were used as at Waterloo. At main-line junctions such as Havant, Horsham, Guildford and Woking the very distinctive position-light junction indicators were to be seen. These indicators have a sighting range very little inferior to that of the day colour-light signals, and they were found of estimable value at a location such as Havant, where non-stopping trains on the coast line approach at high speed. At terminal stations where semaphore signals were used, the route indicators giving the platform numbers were in some cases of the multiple-lamp type, as at Eastbourne; but more generally indicators were used in which a black figure or letter appeared in front of a white background.

The symbols were electrically selected. The normal aspect when the signal was at danger was a black disc; when the signal was pulled off and a particular route was selected the black disc fell away to a concealed position in the bottom of the case and the symbol required rose into the centre of the viewing ground. The black disc as a normal aspect was used to distinguish between normal and a failure of any of the symbols to rise. Indicators of this type were in service for many years at Waterloo; the largest had a capacity of no fewer than sixteen routes, and when the new colour-light signalling was installed those old indicators were found to be in such good condition that a comparatively small degree of overhaul was necessary to fit them for service elsewhere, though not necessarily with the same number of routes. A modification of this type of indicator was used in the first installation of colour-light signals on the Southern Railway, at Charing Cross and Cannon Street; in order to give an indication of comparable light-intensity the black figure was replaced by a stencil that was pulled into position on the axis of a powerful lens combination. The figure or letter shown was lunar-white on a black ground.

Prior to the extensive works carried out in connection with the electrification of the two routes to Portsmouth, a number of important stations had been equipped with so-called electro-mechanical signalling. Wire-worked semaphore signals and mechanically-worked points were used, but such layouts were track circuited and electrical detection was provided on all points on running lines. Schemes of that kind have very satisfactorily met the requirements at Tonbridge, Hawkesbury Street Junction Dover, Southampton Central, Templecombe and elsewhere. Bognor Regis provided one of the latest examples. In a large number of the electro-mechanical layouts the existing locking frames were adapted for the purpose. On the various sections of the Southern Railway a diversity of types existed, and no little ingenuity was shown in the fitting of the numerous electric lever locks and circuit controllers necessary for the work. One of the most interesting conversions was to be seen at Portsmouth Harbour. The density of traffic during the summer months suggested an all-electric interlocking; construction of a new signal-box alongside the old would not however have been an easy matter, as the line is carried on arches, and so the old Stevens frame was adapted to the work. Apart from the fact that mechanical interlocking between levers was retained, the installation conformed to the most up-to-date power signalling practice standard on the Southern Railway, using colour-light signals, multiple-lamp route indicators, solenoid-operated shunt signals and electric point machines throughout. As with all colour-light signals worked from mechanical locking frames, all aspects were repeated in the cabin by means of miniature illuminated indicators mounted on a shelf behind the levers.

Many of the busiest Southern routes include stretches of severe grading. In such instances the slower travelling of trains on the ascending road automatically increases the minimum headway, and with manual block signalling or lock and block, no remedy existed save that of installing intermediate block posts, although the extra signals are needed on one road only. An interesting solution to this problem has been found which was later adopted generally on British Railways. Halfway between two block posts there was installed a two-aspect colour-light stop signal. Although in practice that signal constituted an intermediate block post—and it was accordingly preceded by a distant signal — it was actually an advanced starter for the box in rear. A neat arrangement was obtained by mounting the tubular-steel signal mast on the top of the location case containing all the apparatus. A notable case where such intermediate section signalling greatly eased an acute traffic problem was on the Sole Street bank, where the Eastern Section main line from Ramsgate to London climbs westwards out of the Medway Valley and the gradient is 1 in 100 for five miles. With the heavy trains from the Kent coast resorts, speed with steam traction was rarely more than 30 m.p.h., and at times of pressure delays often occurred because of the long time taken to clear the block sections. On the two routes to Portsmouth, intermediate section signalling is to be found on the heavy gradients leading to the summit at Haslemere on the Direct line, and also on the former L.B. and S.C.R. route between Dorking and

Horsham, where there are appreciable lengths graded between 1 in 90 and 1 in 100.

*   *   *   *   *   *

The Great Western put into service large installations of colour-light signalling in connection with the station reconstructions at Paddington, Bristol Temple Meads, and Cardiff. In all cases the searchlight type of signal was used, but while these three large areas were completely track-circuited and fully equipped with power-worked points, the system of signalling remained essentially that of manual block, while the aspects displayed were the same as the night indications of semaphore signals. So far as drivers were concerned no new code of aspects had to be learned. Two search-light units, one vertically above the other on a single mast, were simply a 'stop' and 'distant' signal in combination. None of the searchlight mechanisms included more than two positions, and in the instance just mentioned the upper unit would display either green or red, as required, and the lower one green, or yellow.

Block working was in operation between all signal-boxes, and the power interlocking frames were designed to incorporate on their facia-boards, a miniature form of block instrument. At Cardiff and Bristol there were large signal-boxes at each end of the stations, and although the whole areas were track-circuited and controlled by colour-light signalling, the link between the two boxes was in each case by block working. At that stage in Great Western history it was evident that no trend towards multi-aspect signalling had commenced. Manual block, with each signal unit—whether sema-phore or searchlight—displaying only two indications, remained completely standard. In Blackall's time some experiments had been made with three-position upper-quadrant signals, and the 'advanced starter' on the down departure line at Paddington was of this type for many years. But with the change-over to colour-lights it was replaced.

CHAPTER X

Automatic Train Control

If an analysis were made summarizing the causes of accidents on the railways of Great Britain, it would be found that an overwhelmingly high proportion had been caused by one of three reasons: either through a driver's error in not observing, or misreading signals, or in running at excessive speed, or through a signalman's error. Serious accidents have also been caused by totally extraneous circumstances, like the accidental fly-shunting of a wagon on to the main line at Chelford, on Christmas Eve, 1894, or the falling of a platform barrow on to the line in front of a Midland express at Wellingborough. But such events are much in the minority. The risk of signalmen's errors were being gradually reduced by improvements in the technique of signalling control and block working, but by the beginning of the 1930s little had been done on the British railways as a whole to lessen the risk of driver's errors. The Great Western Railway, with its system of audible cab signalling, was a notable exception, but at that time British railway officers were not by any means agreed that the Great Western system was the best that could be devised for general use in the country.

There were many divergent views as to how control should be applied. In some quarters it was felt that some form of cab indication was enough and that actual control, in any form, was undesirable. Much British thinking at that time had as a background the very rapid developments that were taking place in America, where the accident record was very much worse than anything sustained in this country. Public opinion had been roused to the extent that the provision of forms of automatic train control were made compulsory over certain lines, and there is no doubt that new systems were devised and put into service somewhat hastily. On the major railroads of the USA, automatic train control systems could be grouped under the following broad headings:

1. Intermittent control with cab signal indications
2. Continuous control with cab signal indications
3. Continuous control with cab signal indications and abolition of the wayside signals
4. Continuous cab signalling without any speed or brake control
5. Continuous cab signalling without any speed or brake control and without wayside signals.

The continuous inductive train control, with cab indications, provided for an automatic control of the speed according to whether high, medium, or low speeds were demanded. The controls, both for actuating cab signals and for application of the brake, were transferred from the track circuits to the locomotive by an inductive link. Nearly all these American systems were elaborate and involved a large amount of electrical and electro-pneumatic apparatus, and great ingenuity was displayed in the mechanical design of the equipment to make it suitable for conveyance on steam locomotives, and thus to be subject to all the racking and vibration inherent in the running of such locomotives.

British engineers, in studying the various systems that were devised in America, and in riding on the locomotives for observation purposes, were not so much concerned with the elaboration of the systems or the amount of gear that had to be carried, but with the simple fact that there was a signal indication to be observed *inside* the engine cab. In Great Britain it has always been a guiding principle of train running that the driver must observe the wayside signals. Anything else that was provided to help the driver should be regarded as a subsidiary and not a substitute, and it was felt that the provision of a visual indicator in the cab could prove a distraction from the driver's first duty, namely, to observe the state of the line ahead and the fixed signals. At a period roughly marked by the year 1930, Sir Nigel Gresley, Chief Mechanical Engineer of the L.N.E.R. and one of the greatest figures in British locomotive practice, came out most strongly against the provision of any form of visual indicator in the cab. On his appointment in 1923, consequent upon the formation of the L.N.E.R., he had inherited from the N.E.R. the rather elaborate cab signalling system developed by Raven and his former assistant, Baister. Quite a number of North Eastern locomotives were equipped with the Raven cab signalling system, which had semaphore indicators in the engine cab, repeating the indications of certain signals along the line. Gresley viewed these with the greatest disfavour and, as a prominent member of the Ministry of Transport Automatic Train Control Committee of 1927, strongly influenced the report that was issued by that committee in 1930.

At that time the system standardized on the Great Western Railway was coming to be regarded much more favourably than had been so when it was first introduced in the early nineteen-hundreds. Although, in 1930, its application on the Great Western was still no more than limited, that company had by far the best record for safe working of any railway in Great Britain. The system itself was essentially safe, in that any failure of the equipment would lead to a more restrictive indication being given to the driver. The cab signals were entirely audible. There was nothing to distract the driver's attention from his view of the line ahead and the indications for 'all-clear' and 'warning' were so utterly different as not to admit of the slightest confusion. The system is, of course, very well known today and its principles were eventually embodied in the system developed by British Railways after nationalization in 1948. In the 1930s, however, the main argument around the Great Western system was whether it went far enough. It was based entirely on the indication displayed by the distant signal, and it was the indication of the distant signal only that was repeated by audible means in the engine cab. As such it was an extremely valuable adjunct to operation, particularly in foggy weather. The indications were intermittent. On open line they would be received at distances of two to three miles, sometimes even longer. In the light of what was being done in the USA, however, there were people in this country who felt that a cab signal coupled with brake control, based entirely on the distant signal, was not enough. There was also, of course, the very vexed question of the arrangements for cancelling. The operating men of the Great Western Railway argued most strongly that it was a first principle of working that the driver should always have complete control of his train. It was undesirable to install any auxiliary system which took control out of his hands, and therefore the indications given in the cab were regarded as no more than an 'alert'. Only if he failed to heed the audible signal corresponding with an adverse 'distant' was control taken out of his hands and the brakes applied to bring the train to rest. Engineers and operating men of other administrations pointed out that there was nothing to stop a driver, who was not properly attending to his duties, from receiving the warning indication, promptly acknowledging it on the lever provided, forestalling the brake application and continuing to run at full speed. This was true enough; but Great Western practice in those days set considerable store on the sense of high responsibility shown by their enginemen and signalmen, and the possibility of such a serious occurrence as a driver acknowledging a warning and then taking no notice of it was thought to be so remote as not to need consideration.

Another factor that came in for a great deal of consideration at the time was the confining of the cab signalling system to the distant signals. Some engineers argued, with statistical evidence to support them, that among all the cases of passing signals at danger a high proportion had occurred at home and starting signals, and not only through misinterpretation or tardy recognition of distant signals. Equally it was argued that cab signalling arrangements based on the distant signal were of such an intermittent nature as to be worth little in operating, and that continuous indication was the only *desideratum* worth aiming at. But, of course, any form of continuous indication immediately brought in the factor of visual signals in the engine cab, and the idea of these was generally disliked in Great Britain.

There was also the question of expense. The 1930s were a time of great financial stringency in Great Britain, and the systems of continuous inductive train control, with or without cab signalling, were very costly. In the USA they had been developed as a result of legal obligations placed upon certain of the railways, and presumably some of the cost would have been borne by the state. In England, however, the system of automatic train control developed on the Great Western was relatively cheap, and when that company, like the others, was asked to undertake schemes for the relief of unemployment, it was found possible, from the funds made available by Government loan, to equip the entire main-line network of the Great Western with the system already well developed and which worked with complete regularity and success.

The stumbling-block towards its general adoption in Great Britain was, of course, the fact that the link between the engine and the wayside signals was made through a contact ramp. Engineers of other administrations felt that such an arrangement of 'pick-up' would be liable to fail in conditions of ice and snow, and that in any case the use of a contact system would entail heavy wear and tear upon the parts coming into contact, often at very high speed. The Great Western was able to brush off such criticism quite easily from the service records of the apparatus already installed; but the fact that other administrations, having decided that the principle of the Great Western system was suitable for their needs, began to develop other systems of 'pick-up', was perhaps yet another demonstration of that traditional individualism on British Railways—one might almost call it parochialism—which refused to adopt, without change, something that has been proved a great success on another railway. Be that as it may, the trial of the Strowger-Hudd inductive system on the Southern Railway was watched with particular interest both by the L.M.S. and the L.N.E. railways, and before the decade was out a modified form of the Hudd system had been put into service on the Southend line of the L.M.S.

The northern lines came in for a great deal of criticism in their apparent reluctance to adopt the Great Western system in its entirety, particularly in that they sustained a series of accidents which the Great Western system would almost certainly have prevented. By far the worst of these was the terrible rear-end collision at Castlecary on the Edinburgh – Glasgow main line, when one express ran at almost full speed into the rear of another in conditions of very bad visibility in snow on a late winter afternoon. As a result of this, and the deep concern shown by the public, the Edinburgh – Glasgow section was chosen for a large-scale experimental installation of the Hudd system that was to be sponsored jointly by both the L.N.E.R. and the L.M.S., basing the details on the experience gained with the L.M.S. installation on the Southend line. Unfortunately the outbreak of war in September 1939 brought this important project to a stand.

On the Southern Railway, although the first installation of the

Strowger-Hudd system had been made on the former L.S.W.R. line near Byfleet, which was then entirely steam-operated, the need for some form of adjunct to the wayside signals was generally considered to be small. In the London suburban areas, where traffic was most intense, and where in fog and other conditions of poor visibility accidents were most likely to occur through the over-running of signals, all important lines were being equipped, stage by stage, with three-aspect and four-aspect colour-light signals. By reason of the close headways worked, these signals had to be very closely spaced—on certain lines no more than 600 yards apart; and it was considered that this very spacing of the signals and the need for drivers to be so constantly on the look-out was breeding a degree of alertness and concentration on the part of enginemen that virtually rendered any additional system of warning unnecessary. In consequence the programme of development on the Southern Railway generally provided for the gradual extension of multi-aspect colour-light signals, and not for any form of cab signalling or automatic train control.

The position at the outbreak of war in 1939 on the British railways could thus be summarized as follows:

1. On the Great Western the system of audible cab signalling with automatic train control based on the distant signals was virtually complete over the entire main-line network, and nearly all locomotives owned by the company were equipped with the necessary apparatus.

2. On the L.M.S. and the L.N.E.R. a development of the Strowger-Hudd system was favoured and engineering work was in progress to render this system suitable for general adoption; but at the outbreak of war nothing more than a trial installation had been made on the L.T. and S. line of the L.M.S.

3. The Southern Railway had decided that extension of the system of multi-aspect colour-light signals, with the close spacing between signals demanded by the intensity of the train service, would meet all requirements in the foreseeable future.

All the above discussion relates, of course, to main-line working and the working of fast outer-suburban services such as those operated on most London area lines of the Southern Railway. One cannot leave the subject of automatic train control, however, without some reference to the totally different system standardized on the electric railways of what was then the London Passenger Transport Board, and which had been adopted also on certain surface lines where underground trains ran over the tracks of one or other of the main-line companies. The problem on these so-called 'rapid-transit' lines was different and generally much simpler. For one thing maximum speeds were lower; all trains ran at the same speed, and all had the same braking power. It is also important to recall that the need to provide some very positive form of A.T.C. on these lines was imperative from the outset, because with smart running electric trains, on tube railways, the consequences of a 'run through' of signals would be unthinkable. There could be no question of alerting a driver to the existence of danger ahead and relying on him to act upon it. The control must be irrevocably automatic.

Accordingly on the London underground lines the system of A.T.C. was based not on the distant but on the stop signals, and co-acting with every signal was an automatic train-stop. If the signal was in the danger position the train-stop arm would be raised to such a height that it would engage with a hanging lever on the train. Passage over a train-stop in the raised position and the actuation of the hanging lever actuated the trip valve and made an emergency application of the brakes. Once a train has been thus tripped the driver can do nothing about it. The signals are so spaced that an emergency stop following such a run over a raised train stop would bring the train to rest in a distance clear of any preceding train, or of the fouling point at a junction. If the signal is in the 'clear' position, the train-stop arm is lowered and no contact is made with the trip lever as the train passes by. This again is an intermittent system being based on control at each home signal; but as a train travelling at the fastest speed on the line can be stopped short of any fouling point or obstruction when the trip valve is operated, one has virtually a continuous form of control, although it is applied only at specific points on the line.

This system was developed on the Metropolitan and the Metropolitan District Railways in the London area, and was installed throughout the tube system of London. Its use has been extended, as previously mentioned, to cover outdoor sections where underground electric trains run, such as Queens Park to Watford on the former L.N.W.R., used by trains of the Bakerloo tube, on one section of the L.T. and S. line as far as Upminster, used by the District Railway trains, and on the Ealing and Shepherd's Bush line of the Great Western, used by Central London tube trains. This system had by the 1930s been developed to a very high degree of reliability, and the only fatal accident that has occurred to a passenger train on the London underground system in the past forty-five years was due not to any inherent failure of signal apparatus, but to an error in the wiring following the replacement of certain parts in the course of routine maintenance work.

CHAPTER XI

A Retrospect and a Pause

The outbreak of war in 1939 soon brought all active developments in British signalling to a stand. From the outset it was realized that engineering would play a predominant part in the conflict, whether in the development of direct armaments or in providing for transport of men and materials. Railways would be a legitimate and obvious target for enemy air attacks, and in modern conditions the greater the concentration of control at a few large centres the greater could be the dislocation and chaos if a major centre were destroyed or severely damaged. In September 1939 work on a number of very large schemes was in progress. This was very soon suspended, because the attention of railway staff was largely taken up with providing protective measures against damage to existing works, and because contractors were required to do other work. Furthermore, the completion of large centres, where control over a wide area was concentrated, was merely to create vulnerable targets.

At the time there was not much opportunity for reflection, to view in retrospect the achievements of the years since grouping. But at this distance in time the pause in development can be regarded in something of its true perspective, seeing British practice as it stood in 1939 in relation to contemporary happenings on the continent of Europe and farther afield. The outstanding development was of course that of relay interlocking, and in this field British practice had already drawn so far ahead of every other country using power signalling as to be virtually the *only* country to have applied it other than in an experimental state. In this respect relay interlocking proper must not be confused with panel operation, using thumb-switches and push-buttons.

GLOUCESTER ROAD
JUNCTION, SOUTHERN
RAILWAY

42.
One of the most complicated
post-war interlockings in the
pre-panel era

43. The pioneer panel route interlocking at Thirsk, L.N.E.R.

EVOLUTION IN CONTROL PANEL STYLING

44. The handsomely styled control panel at Tonbridge, Southern Region

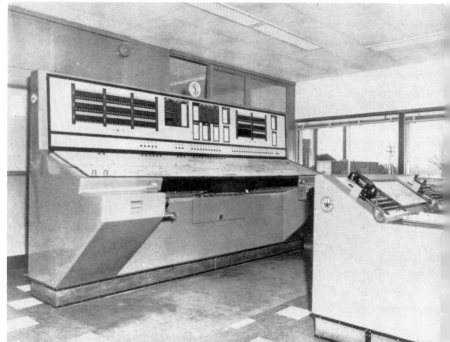

Chelford, Manchester – Crewe line, remotely controlled from Sandbach

MODERN ELECTRO-MECHANICAL PLANTS

Stobcross Junction, Glasgow Area, with mechanical levers for points
and thumb-switches on diagram for signal controls

47. Chislehurst Junction, Southern Region

MODERN SIGNAL-BOX ARCHITECTURE

48. Manchester Piccadilly, with relay-room in the
arches of the viaduct

The use of panels, as distinct from power interlocking frames, had progressed to a remarkable extent in the North Eastern Area of the L.N.E.R. by the year 1939, and on the very day war broke out one of the most interesting of these installations was brought into service, namely, that at Northallerton. This panel interlocking formed part of the resignalling of the East Coast main line, and extended the work previously done between York and Northallerton farther north by some fourteen miles to Darlington. This scheme as a whole was interesting, because opportunity was taken of installing for comparative purposes a lever interlocking frame with electric interlocking at Darlington South. In the fourteen miles between Northallerton and Darlington there were only three signal-boxes: the two complete power interlockings at each end of the section, a panel interlocking at Northallerton and the all-electric lever interlocking frame at Darlington; and at the junction of the Richmond branch at Eryholme five miles south of Darlington there was an electro-mechanical interlocking with panel working for the signals and mechanical levers for the points. At Eryholme the interlocking between the signal operation and the points operation was entirely electric, through the agency of electric lever locks on the tails of the mechanical point levers.

The experience gained with the panel interlockings in the North Eastern Area of the L.N.E.R. and with the lever interlocking frame at Darlington convinced the railway officers in that area of the superiority in general operation of the panel type of interlocking, and by the outbreak of war the contract had already been let for installation of the huge panel interlocking at York. Thus, to summarize the position in the North Eastern Area in 1939, the installations already in commission were as follows:

Location	Type of Relay Interlocking
Thirsk	Route relay interlocking with individual route switches on the actual illuminated diagram.
Leeds East	Electro-mechanical: individual signal operation by thumb switch on panel. Points operated mechanically.
Leeds West	Relay interlocking with individual operation of all points and signals; switches for both points and signals mounted on the diagram.

H

Hull Paragon   Route relay interlocking with one control switch for each route; switches mounted on a console below the illuminated diagram.

Northallerton   Route relay interlocking with one control switch for each route; switches mounted on console below the diagram. First use of white route-lights to indicate route which had been set.

Based on the experience obtained with the above installations, the York panel, for which the design work had been commenced in 1939, was the same as that used at Northallerton except that it was some four times the size. In complexity it could be compared more closely to the panel at Hull, which was a terminal station with many intersecting and shunt movements, whereas Northallerton was a main-line running junction covering a considerable mileage of track, but mainly dealing with through non-stopping movements. The physical size of the panels at Northallerton and Hull were roughly the same, but whereas Northallerton panel included 129 routes, the panel at Hull included 230. By comparison with these two, the new panel in course of design for York included no fewer than 825 routes, and it was arranged to have a panel in four facets, each approximately the same size as the one panel at Hull.

Outside the North Eastern Area of the L.N.E.R. nothing comparable had been done at that time in Great Britain, though the transfer of Mr Tattersall from the North Eastern Area to the Southern Area of the L.N.E.R. in 1937 led to the development of some very interesting projects for panel working which, however, did not come to fruition until after the war.

In comparison with this striking wholly-British development in the art of power interlocking, virtually nothing of a similar kind was to be seen outside Great Britain in 1939. Although some very large new plants were being brought into use on the railways of the USA, and interesting developments were taking place on railways on the continent of Europe, all these included lever, or slide interlocking frames of the conventional types hitherto used in these countries, and all included mechanical interlocking between the operating members. It was not until after the war that British practice in respect of all-electric interlocking on lever frames, and relay interlocking on control panels, began to be adopted on the continent of Europe. During the war certain panel interlockings were introduced in America, but they came at a time when British development had been virtually brought to a halt by war conditions.

At the same time American developments in panel interlockings had progressed to a notable degree in another way altogether. In the 1920s the system of coded remote control, commonly known as C.T.C., had been pioneered and the system had been found extremely effective in dealing with certain of the long stretches of single-line railway that existed in the Middle West and Western States of the USA. It is important to appreciate the conditions in which this system was first introduced, because a sustained attempt was at one time made to interest British railway administrations in the same system. The great majority of these long, sparsely-used trans-continental lines originally had no signalling at all and traffic was regulated entirely by means of telegraphic train orders. Although the 'train order' system of working can be very effective, and very economical so far as staff and equipment is concerned, it can lead to a certain amount of delay in handling traffic, and the availability of C.T.C. led some of the leading railways to install plant for handling trains on these single lines for the first time by signal indication, rather than by written train orders handed to the engine crews.

The system of control can be likened to the early days of automatic telephone switching. Some systems used a two-wire transmission, others three-wire, but the basis of the system was a coded control. The operator wishing to move a pair of points, or clear a signal at some distant location, turned a switch, and this had the effect of 'dialling' the number on the line wires from the central office to the remote locations. The signals and points at each remote station were fully interlocked with each other and controlled by track circuit, so that a high degree of safety was immediately introduced into the workings which had not existed previously. But the system had the great disadvantage that the central operator, who might be supervising up to 150 miles of single-line railway, could only 'dial' one function at a time. The sending of a code took approximately four seconds, and a similar time elapsed for the indication to come back to the central office showing by appropriate lights on the central illuminated diagram that the function had actually responded to what the operator had required. It will therefore be appreciated that with every control code taking four seconds to be sent out, and every indication code taking four seconds to return, there was a definite limit to the amount of control that could be exercised by a central office.

For the single-line railways in the USA the system was ideal. Many of these lines had only two or three passenger trains a day in each direction and probably that number of freight trains in addition. On the control panel, covering 150 miles of line, there would probably never be more than two or three trains at once, and no congestion would take place in the sending or receipt of codes. The system was to prove of inestimable value when the war with Japan broke out and vast quantities of material and services personnel had to be conveyed to the Pacific coast. The lines already equipped with C.T.C. were able to handle far more traffic than they had previously dealt with, while others were specially equipped to enable them to deal with the wartime traffic. Great interest was taken in the progressively more spectacular installations of C.T.C. being made in America, and serious concern was given to the application of the system to certain stretches of single-line railway in Great Britain. There were, for example, lines in the Highlands of Scotland which seemed very suitable for the introduction of C.T.C., notably the West Highland, the section of the Highland main line north of Inverness and the Dingwall and Skye line of the Highland Railway. It seemed as though all these three lines could be operated through a single control panel, thus eliminating all the existing intermediate signal-boxes, the necessity for tablet working and the staffs involved.

In giving further consideration to these lines, however, the essential difference between Scotland and the Middle West of America became more clearly appreciated. The lines in Scotland were fully signalled; all the stations were interlocked and all these lines were equipped with electric single-line token apparatus. On the Highland main line north of Inverness there was the further facility of mechanical token exchange. At the majority of intermediate stations in remote parts of the Highlands the signalmen combined their duties with those of porter and sometimes of stationmaster, and as at that time all these stations were open and dealing with traffic the savings in staff that might be realized by

116

installations of the American type of C.T.C. appeared to be no more than small. Furthermore C.T.C. necessarily required continuous track circuiting of all these lines and would involve maintenance work, including new skills which would have to be learned. It is true that C.T.C. offered the promise of considerable improvement in traffic working, by the substitution of central supervision from a single control panel for the previous British control methods; but the summing up of the situation as it appeared during the war years was that the American type of C.T.C. would not greatly benefit railway working as a whole on the sections of single line existing in this country—at any rate in the conditions of operation and traffic then prevailing.

Reverting to the pioneer British work in relay interlocking for large stations and junctions, the development in the 1930s provides a parallel to the early British developments of interlocking itself, and of closed-block working in Victorian times. Great Britain was a pioneer in the construction of railways and in the development of safe methods of working; in Victorian times British railway methods were a model upon which practice in many parts of the world was based. In the 1930s the development of relay interlocking was a pioneer work no less momentous and important than that which had taken place between sixty and seventy years earlier. It is unfortunate that the onset of war dropped the curtain on this development and to a large extent obscured its significance. Certainly, when the war was over, other countries, notably the USA, had gone ahead with signalling practice which to some extent robbed Great Britain of her lead; and while some European countries whose railways had been so damaged by successive campaigns fought over them came to study our methods, that period of rebuilding gave an opportunity for entirely fresh thinking, in which wartime work in the USA, the pre-war experience of Great Britain and the individual needs of countries on the continent of Europe resulted in a crop of new forms of relay interlocking being developed.

After the war, from being the outright pioneer Great Britain found herself being merely one of many countries developing the art of relay interlocking. Nevertheless the achievements of the late 1930s are ones of solid fact and not merely a propagation of ideas. The installations at Thirsk, Leeds, Hull and Northallerton were major technological advances in signalling practice. If work had been able to continue with the installation at York as originally programmed, and completion had been possible about the year 1942, it would certainly have ranked among the railway wonders of the world. As it was, because the conditions of austerity imposed on Great Britain after the war had such a deadening effect upon all new developments and upon plans for extensive investment, it was not brought into service until 1951.

CHAPTER XII

The Years of Austerity

This is no place to dwell upon the factors—political and others—that plunged this country into six or seven years of economic gloom, continuance of food rationing, and conditions that did not however damp the traditional British sense of good humour enough to prevent the coining of a slogan like 'Britain can lump it'. After the colossal effort this country had put into the war effort, it was galling in the extreme to find our own plans for post-war development blocked for lack of ready capital, and still more galling to hear 'clever fellows' pointing out how much quicker other countries were progressing. There was considerable delay in getting restarted many of the signalling schemes that had been suspended during the war. The great relay interlocking at York was too far advanced to permit of major changes without quite inordinate additional expense; but its companion and sequel at Newcastle was held up for a long time, pending a decision as to where the signal-box itself was to be located. In those early days after the war strategic considerations still loomed large, and for a time it was proposed to have the box and its relay-room far underground. One of the first new installations to be commissioned after the war was at Doncaster, and it embodied one of the last innovations for which A. E. Tattersall was responsible.

In the relay interlockings commissioned before the war, and equally in those on which work had been suspended, one very prominent feature had been the large increase in quantity of relays over one of the former conventional types of power interlocking using a miniature-lever frame. While panel operation provided far greater compactness, and the possibility of bringing infinitely larger areas than previously under the control of one signal-box, the size of relay-rooms had more than doubled, despite the introduction of certain special multi-contact interlocking relays. Tattersall, perhaps more than anyone else, was aware of this trend, and shortly before the outbreak of war he was actively developing the so-called 'sequence switch' type of interlocking. Mounted behind the panel there was a single rotary switch at the true geographical position of each pair of facing points. These rotary switches could be rotated to positions corresponding to the different routes to which the points concerned could read. After the switch had been turned to the desired position the setting up of a route was initiated by the pressing of a plunger incorporated in that portion of the switch that was above the panel. The routes leading from any pair of points would naturally be conflicting, and would require locking one against the other, and in earlier relay interlockings many additional relays were necessary to do this. But in this clever invention, the nature of the rotary switch, and the simple though fundamental fact that it could not be in two positions at once, provided a natural interlock, and greatly reduced the number of relays required in any one installation.

The system was applied at Doncaster, in a notable installation brought into service in January 1949. To many students of signalling and operating practice however it was a little surprising that the whole layout had not been arranged on one panel, particularly in view of the philosophy preached so vigorously by Mr Tattersall in the past. But, of course, in Great Britain the last word does not necessarily lie with the signal engineer. He is not the user. The signalmen are in the operating department, and on the London and North Eastern Railway there had always been a very deep cleavage of opinion between the operating authorities of the Southern and North Eastern Areas respectively. At York, C. M. Jenkin-Jones and his very forceful successor A. P. Hunter favoured one box; in the Southern Area, Barrington-Ward was always reluctant to put all his signalling eggs into one basket. And so Tattersall, of all men, had to install his pioneer installation of sequence switch interlocking in two boxes at Doncaster. Actually he had retired in 1948, before the job was commissioned. By that time the former Southern Area of the L.N.E.R. had become the Eastern Region of British Railways, and the sequence-switch interlocking system, despite its ingenuity, was not perpetuated in future installations.

Some of the most important works put into commission during the period of austerity after the war were in the London suburban areas of the Southern. The inner area of the former South Eastern lines, from St John's inwards to Cannon Street and Charing Cross, had been modernized in 1926-9; the approaches to Waterloo on the former L.S.W.R. had been modernized by 1936, and following the electrification of the Brighton line, and the installation of colour-light signals throughout from Coulsdon to Brighton itself, a start had been made, in 1938, with the inner suburban area, centred upon Victoria. The lines from Coulsdon inwards, including the eastern prong of the bifurcation from East Croydon which led through Forest Hill and New Cross Gate to the Brighton terminus at London Bridge, were fully equipped with Sykes 'lock and block' apparatus. The actual signals were all semaphores, but the block sections were mostly short, to provide for close-headway working in the rush hours. It was considered that the 'lock and block' equipment provided additional safeguards in working, and so, in preparing the programme for complete signalling modernization, after the 'country' section between Coulsdon and Brighton had been completed, the terminus would be dealt with first in the inner area, leaving the section between Battersea and Coulsdon to follow. Victoria and the new 'fringe' box at Battersea Park were commissioned in 1938-9, but even before this work was completed a serious accident had occurred at Battersea Park that highlighted a danger in the Sykes system, as it was then being operated on the Southern Railway.

The Southern Railway had done more than any other company in Great Britain to modernize its signalling and operating methods in the London suburban area, where in general the working during the morning and evening rush hours was of an intensity unparalleled anywhere else in the world; and it was extremely bad luck that a signalman's error should have occurred on one of the few remaining sections where modern equipment had not yet been installed. The section from Battersea Park to Coulsdon was indeed high on the priority list for attention, but with the outbreak of war in September 1939 the plans were shelved. On resumption afterwards the extensive re-signalling to complete the equipment of the Brighton main lines was carried out in accordance with the well-established Southern practice, using miniature-lever power frames and large illuminated track diagrams with the spotlight type of indication for showing track circuit occupancy. One of the most interesting of the new signal-boxes was that at Gloucester Road Junction, which controls the 'complex' of intersections where the Victoria and London Bridge main lines converge, just to the north of East Croydon.

Both lines are quadruple-tracked and very heavily utilized in the peak periods. Complications in track layout exist because of the position of the 'through' or fast lines on the Victoria and London Bridge routes respectively, and the position of the through lines after the convergence at East Croydon. The divergence of the route to Sutton via West Croydon had also to be provided for, also access to the Norwood electric car sheds, certain goods yards, and the Norwood fork whereby there is direct connection from Norwood Junction to Selhurst. The former London Brighton and South Coast railway had over the years developed a very efficient system of burrowing and flying junctions in this area, to avoid surface connections of conflicting movements as far as possible, and the working of the area in mechanical days, with 'lock and block' and signal-boxes at every individual junction, was a masterpiece of organization and collaboration between all the boxes concerned. The intense traffic flowed very smoothly. The new power box at Gloucester Road Junction, covering the whole area, has a miniature-lever frame of 131 levers, and it replaced four mechanical boxes having a total of 235 levers between them. The opening of this new box in 1954, and the final one in the programme—East Croydon—in 1955, completed the provision of colour-light signalling throughout to Brighton, from both the major London terminal stations. It proved a milestone in another respect, that these were the last major Southern re-signalling schemes to have the miniature-lever type of control machine. All future schemes included control panels, with either push-button or miniature thumb-switch actuation.

The other large modernization project, the completion of which was postponed because of the war, was the signalling in connection with the electrification of the Great Eastern suburban lines. The signalling scheme was originally prepared by Mr A. E. Tattersall, and was completed in August 1949 by his successor, Mr A. Moss. Liverpool Street station itself was perhaps the classic example of the optimum operating performance that could be achieved in suburban traffic with steam traction and mechanical signalling.

The signalling itself was installed in 1895, by McKenzie and Holland Ltd, with Sykes lock and block, and at the maximum intensity of traffic the station handled fifty trains an hour. The new signalling work completed in 1949 covered the thirteen and a half route miles between Gidea Park and Liverpool Street, and for its execution three contracts were let. While the system of signal aspects and traffic facilities were, of course, the same throughout, no attempt was made to standardize the means whereby that end was achieved. The relay interlockings at Liverpool Street, Stratford, Goodmayes and elsewhere were each of the contractors' own design. This was of considerable interest at the time, when each successive installation was being examined eagerly for signs and portents towards future British standards; but in retrospect the Great Eastern Colchester main line now represents a somewhat heterogenous collection of apparatus—much of types that have not since been perpetuated to any appreciable extent. At the time there was an urgent need to get the electrification work completed and to have endeavoured to achieve standardization between the work of three signalling contractors would have led to inadmissible delay. In any case, whatever degree of standardization might then have been achieved on that one section of line could have been no more than transient.

The nationalization of the railways of Britain, as from January 1, 1948, foreshadowed the eventual unification of practice, not only in signalling but in every other facet of railway engineering work. But the initial stages involved no more than a systematic collation of existing practices by the newly set up staff at Railway Executive headquarters. The gathering of the material was a colossal task in itself quite apart from the subsequent studying and sifting that would be necessary before a national policy could be evolved. Furthermore, personnel were constantly changing, and anyone who has studied the history of railway engineering in Great Britain, in whatever field he may have chosen, will have become intensely aware of the extent to which personal preferences have furthered or overturned existing policies. So, by and large, nationalization did not have any immediate influence upon signalling engineering practice, and when the great plan for general modernization of the railways was launched, the various regions made their own plans and formulated their own detailed policies.

CHAPTER XIII

Modernization on the Grand Scale

In the late autumn of 1956 there was issued a White Paper on 'Proposals for the Railways'. This long-awaited plan for modernization provided for capital investment on a vast scale, on electrification, on the substitution elsewhere of diesel for steam motive power, for the fitting of continuous brakes on all freight trains, the construction of many new mechanized marshalling yards, and a programme of re-signalling geared to fit in with the other facets of modernization. Looking back, after twelve years, to the appendix to the Modernization Plan, in which details of the programme were set out, and reflecting upon all that has happened in the intervening years, it was perhaps significant of the status previously held by the signal engineering profession that the signalling works, although expected to cost some £12,000,000 a year from 1958 onwards, came last in the programme, and that much of it was referred to as an adjunct to other features of the plan—notably electrification and the construction of marshalling yards. The appendix to the White Paper concluded: 'This will require a considerable expansion in the output of signalling manufacturers and contractors, who are aware of the need.'

We were indeed! Perhaps for a few sentences I may be permitted to intrude upon the general story with some personal memories of those exciting days. For years we had been soldiering along with a relatively small staff; many of these were men of quite long service, well trained, specialists in their various fields, while some had run the whole gauntlet of signalling work—in workshops, drawing offices, circuit designing and installation, both in Great Britain and in far corners of the world. Then, with very little warning, we had to build up virtually to *treble* our previous maximum output. It was a tremendous challenge, the kind of prospect hitherto beyond our wildest dreams, but at the same time a dream that often looked like becoming a nightmare. There were immense problems in recruitment and administration. Premises had to be found and be adapted as drawing offices; experienced men, who had been used to working as individuals, did not always take kindly to laying aside their own instruments and supervising the efforts of an ever-growing stream of raw recruits. Regional centres which had previously been able to undertake all their own installation work found themselves in uncharted seas when faced with the need for putting much of such work out to contract, in order to meet the completion dates demanded by the 'plan'.

It was an exciting time for all. In the early stages a degree of inter-regional standardization took place—not because of some overriding directive, but because the acceptance of existing designs of equipment was the only way in which deliveries could be matched to installation programmes. But from the very outset there was one thing that could not be standardized, and that of course was the individual track layouts. A large labour force was built up purely for the drawing of illuminated track diagrams, and as the work gained momentum so the problems of finding physical space to make these large diagrams became more acute. There were numerous incidental worries, as when newcomers to the industry could not understand why the practice of display in the XYZ Region was not acceptable to the U. & V.W.! In our own rural district of Wessex we gathered in staff 'from the highways and hedges'. Village maidens, who in another age would have been farm-hands or dairy maids, were trained to do the fine lettering needed on illuminated diagrams, or to draw printed circuits. We were, of course, not alone in our staff and training problems. I remember discussing things with an associate in the Birmingham district, and said we were taking on anyone who could make marks on paper. 'Marks on paper!' he retorted, 'Up here if a chap can sharpen a pencil he's in!'

To the majority of signal engineers in middle age it was the opportunity and excitement of a lifetime. For decades we had extolled the advantages in operation to be obtained from modern signalling installed on the grand scale, and now suddenly we had to do it, in almost breathless haste. The timetable for the first wave of modernization in all regions left little time for the working out of practices standard to all of them; the operating requirements differed widely, and each region had its own ideas on the kind of apparatus to be installed. In a very short time my own drawing office was loaded to capacity—and beyond!—with new design work on contracts located variously between the South London Suburban and Berwick-upon-Tweed and between Shoeburyness, Manchester and Glasgow. Mine was no exception. Simultaneously also was launched the conception of a nation-wide system of new highly-mechanized marshalling yards to replace the vast proliferation of small, hand-controlled yards in the old style, which absorbed so much manpower, took so much time over the job, and created quite a lot of damage to both rolling stock and contents. The philosophy of the mechanized marshalling yard is a subject of its own, and one which signal engineers played a large part in creating. A separate chapter is devoted to this notable phase in signal engineering history.

In its first onslaught the emphasis of the Modernization Plan lay upon electrification, and three major projects were immediately put in hand. These were the extension of the Southern standard system to embrace all main routes in the county of Kent; the London suburban area, and Southend lines of the former Great Eastern Railway; and the long cherished plan for electrifying the main line out of Euston. The first of these would in the ordinary way have been little more than a routine job. The signal department of the former Southern Railway had a magnificent organization, built up on the experience of modernization works dating back to Charing Cross and Cannon Street, in 1926, and taking in its stride projects like the Brighton and Portsmouth main-line electrifications, and the most recent developments in the London suburbs, linking the colour-light signalling at the terminal stations of Victoria and London Bridge with the main-line signalling south of Croydon. Principles were established, apparatus and circuits largely standardized, and the large interlockings worked by the well-tried Style 'L' power frame, with all-electric interlocking. Only the volume of work presented a new problem, because the entire route between Herne Hill and Ramsgate had to be brought into service in a matter of two years.

Two factors intervened, to make the work on the Southern as

novel and difficult as any undertaken in the whole country at that time. There is no doubt that Lewis Boucher and his staff would like to have continued with the form of interlocking practice that they had used, to the exclusion of all others, for the past quarter of a century. In so doing however they would have made the Southern the 'odd man out'. The precepts of Tattersall were at last finding universal favour on British railways; all other regions were basing their modernization plans on the use of control panels rather than interlocking frames. Furthermore the speed with which the work was demanded made it imperative not only to let the installation out to contract, but to divide it between three different manufacturers. For more than a quarter of a century Southern signalling modernization had been installed on the 'do-it-yourself' principle; but now this otherwise widely-experienced department had to launch into the unfamiliar ground of preparing specifications for contractors, and invigilating on work in progress over the whole line between Herne Hill and Ramsgate. It was also inevitably a time to break with the old traditions so far as control machines were concerned, but having accepted panel operation in principle certain interlockings were equipped with the Westinghouse one-control switch system (O.C.S.) and others on the entrance-exit system, which required two buttons to be operated. It was a difficult time for the Southern. After so many years of standardized interlocking machines they found themselves installing O.C.S. panels, and entrance-exit panels of three different makes! From the drivers' point of view the signalling was exactly the same as previously.

One of the most interesting of the new signal-boxes was at Chislehurst. The system of interconnecting junctions at this point is of historic interest. In the old days of prolonged railway warfare in Kent—Watkin *versus* Forbes—the Chatham main line dived under the South Eastern just to the south of Chislehurst station and there was no connection between the two. One of the earliest results of the 'peace treaty' between the two deadly rivals, and the formation of the South Eastern and Chatham Managing Committee, was the construction of a complete set of interconnecting junctions between the two lines so that one could get virtually from 'anywhere to anywhere'. They were magnificently engineered, with 'fly-unders' to avoid all conflicting surface crossings, and at the four extremities, leading to Bickley and St Mary

Cray on the Chatham, Chislehurst and Orpington on the South Eastern, there were separate signal-boxes. Although the time had not come, in 1957, for the modernization of the signalling on the South Eastern line, the overall planning looked some years ahead and the junction complex in the Bickley, Chislehurst, St Mary Cray, Orpington area was considered as a whole and brought under the control of one signal-box. This was located in an elevated position alongside the South Eastern line, and overlooking the entire complex. It is a fascinating viewpoint from which to watch the trains, although of course nowadays almost all of them are multiple-unit electrics. Other large-panel interlockings were put in at Beckenham, Shortlands, Gillingham, and Faversham. In the less intense areas the Southern followed their previous practice, and installed electro-mechanical interlockings, though with colour-light signals throughout.

At the start of the modernization plan there was no question about the type of electrification to be used on the Southern extensions. The standard 750-volt d.c. system, using third-rail pick-up, had been extended to the Medway towns just before World War II, and this was accepted for the extensions first to Ramsgate, and later to Folkestone and Dover via Tonbridge. Elsewhere in Great Britain things were very different. The long-delayed electrification of the Great Eastern suburban lines had been completed not long after the end of World War II on the system recommended by the Weir Committee, namely 1,500-volt d.c. with overhead line; and the same system had been used for the electrification of the heavily worked Manchester-Sheffield line of the former Great Central, with its north-easterly mineral connection to Wath marshalling yard. The 1,500-volt d.c. overhead system had been installed with great success in Holland, and it was being used for the modernization of the former Paris, Lyons and Mediterranean line in France. When the opportunity for modernization came in Great Britain, however, the French had introduced the 25,000-volt a.c. system, at the commercial frequency of 50 cycles per second, and after the fullest investigation the engineers of the Railway Executive recommended the adoption of this latter system for all future work. This was in 1955.

This covered the projected electrification of the main line from Euston, all of which would be new, but the question arose as to

locking at Birmingham
New Street, London
Midland Region

50.

The neat layout of miniature relay interlocking. Note the complete concealment of all wiring

MODERN
RELAY-ROOM
EQUIPMENT

51.

The packaged units in the geographical circuit layout at Euston

what was to be done on lines where electrification work already completed represented no more than a first stage. This burning question applied particularly to the Great Eastern lines, on which the extension of electrification was authorized to Chingford and Enfield, in the London area, and on the main line to Colchester and Clacton. Authorization was given for the existing 1,500-volt d.c. lines between Liverpool Street and Southend to be converted. This was one of the most difficult tasks given to any signal department on British Railways at that time. Where there is electric traction, and currents infinitely greater than anything used in signalling are flowing, the greatest care has to be taken to render the signalling equipment immune from interference and wrong operation by stray traction current, caused by leakages to earth or otherwise. The signalling on the existing d.c. traction lines used a.c. at a frequency of 50 cycles per second. This provided entirely safe operation with d.c. traction, but it would have been highly vulnerable to the new system traction. Thus, the existing signalling had to be rendered a.c.-immune, and between London and Southend the problem for signal departments was made more difficult because the traction system was planned to be changed over from d.c. to a.c. in a single weekend.

I need not attempt to enlarge here upon the highly technical problems involved in developing arrangements to render the signalling apparatus a.c.-immune. It is enough to say that it entailed the alteration of all the track circuits, much change in wiring in signalbox relay-rooms and lineside apparatus cases, and the virtual rebuilding of all the track circuit relays. While it was essential, for traffic purposes, to effect the traction change-over in a single weekend, the signalling certainly could not be changed in so short a time, and the alteration to track circuits and rebuilding of relays extended over some eight months. Of course, it goes without saying that an immense amount of preparatory work was also necessary on the traction side prior to the actual change-over. The signal department had, stage by stage, carried out the conversion work to their equipment, and relatively little had to be done at the week-end of traction change-over. It was a remarkable piece of engineering planning, about which very little was known at the time, because there was so little to show for it! The colour-light signals were already there.

I

Another major re-signalling programme in the Eastern Region concerned the entire network of the former London, Tilbury and Southend lines, from Fenchurch Street to Shoeburyness, including the Tilbury loop. Here again no vital new principles were involved. It was a case of the most intense planning to ensure that electrification and re-signalling were carried out in such a way as to cause a minimum of disturbance to the very heavy suburban traffic. The comparison between old and new is certainly spectacular. Between Fenchurch Street and Upminster, where the train headway is two minutes, there were previously twenty-two mechanical signal-boxes, with a total of 1,434 levers. This excludes Fenchurch Street itself, where the existing power interlocking frame was retained. Under the new arrangements only one panel box, at Barking, replaced the previous twenty-two boxes. On other parts of the line the working is not so intense, but panel boxes were also installed at Tilbury, Pitsea Junction and Southend Central. An outstanding feature of the whole project was the enormous amount of stage work needed, and this made vital an even more enormous amount of back-stage planning, and the closest co-operation with all other railway departments concerned with the running of the trains. This, although exceptionally intricate in the case of the London Tilbury and Southend lines, was no more typical of much of the signalling work on the Modernization Plan. Many a time senior officers said: 'Oh, we spend all our time at meetings now!' But those meetings were not in vain. The staffs of railway departments and contractors alike worked like beavers, and the arrangements thrashed out at those many meetings were translated into punctual accomplishment.

In Scotland some very interesting work was involved in the Glasgow area. Electrification of the Clyde Coast lines was divided into two stages, north and south of the river, with an additional project covering the heavily worked Cathcart Circle. But it was at Glasgow Central itself that the overall railway problems were of such complexity. Until the year 1879 the Caledonian Railway terminus was at Bridge Street on the south side of the River Clyde, but intense competition from the Glasgow and South Western Railway led to the construction of the first Clyde viaduct and the building of the Central station. At the time the navigational authorities put a limitation upon the width of the railway bridge, and no more than four tracks abreast could be accommodated. But the new bridge and central station gave much relief to the congested layout at Bridge Street—though not for long. In ten years the traffic had virtually doubled. The station itself was enlarged, and then followed the inevitable congestion on the approach lines. So, in 1899, Parliamentary powers were obtained for the *doubling* of the accommodation in the station itself, and for construction of a great new approach viaduct over the Clyde carrying *nine* tracks abreast. This great project was completed in 1908, and the signalling, electro-pneumatic throughout, was appropriately controlled by the largest single-power interlocking frame ever constructed, having 374 levers.

In 1955 Glasgow Central had to be prepared to receive the electric trains from the Cathcart Circle, and for the future electrification of the coast lines to Gourock and Wemyss Bay. Electrification of the West Coast main line down to Carlisle was also freely talked about. And at that same time the civil engineers reached the unwelcome conclusion that the original Clyde bridge of 1879 was rapidly becoming unfit to carry the traffic. Since the enlargement of the station the old bridge had carried the principal main-line express traffic, and the heaviest locomotives; heavy reconstruction work would have been necessary to render the bridge fit for further service. Faced with this difficult situation the whole problem of future working in the station was considered on the broadest basis. Electrification of the Cathcart Circle, and of the Clyde Coast lines, with exclusive use of multiple-unit trains, would greatly reduce the number of engine movements in the station approaches, while the Signal Engineer, L. J. M. Knotts, considered that with reversible road working on all nine tracks over the new Clyde viaduct the line capacity could be greatly increased. So the decision was taken to demolish rather than reconstruct the old Clyde bridge, and to rearrange the tracks so that all traffic in and out of the station passed over the new bridge. The decision provided an interesting example of the way in which modern railway engineering techniques can reduce the amount of expensive fixed equipment necessary to provide the facilities required for running the trains.

The old power-signalling installation of 1908, having given nearly fifty years of service, was worn out, and it was replaced by a panel interlocking of the O.C.S. type. Colour-light signals

131

replaced the old electro-pneumatic semaphores, but electro-pneumatic point operation remained. A distinctive feature of the O.C.S. system of route relay interlocking is the provision of a chain of white lights on the track diagram illuminated to show the extent of each route that has been set; but on the new panel at Glasgow Central, with reversible road working on every track across the Clyde viaduct, it was considered necessary to indicate whether the route was set for an inward or an outward movement. Furthermore there were, in many cases, alternative routes, from an in-going signal, for example, to a particular platform. With the O.C.S. system in the simplest form one turns a route switch, and if that route is free the points line up as required, the signal clears, and the chain of white lights are illuminated on the diagram. If the route is not clear the functions do not respond. At Glasgow Central, speed being the essence of the working, it was essential to save signalmen the time and trouble of 'trying' a route, and then perhaps trying another, and a novel arrangement was devised for taking fullest advantage of the alternative route facilities.

All signals having two or more alternative routes are provided with the following route selection and control devices:

    (a) A push-button for each of its destinations
    (b) A rotary route selection switch
    (c) A signal thumb-switch

all on the console portion of the panel instrument.

The method of operation is as follows. The signalman, wishing to set a route, say, from signal number 57 to platform 7 will first press the destination button associated with number 57 signal labelled 'Platform 7'. The button, which is made of Perspex, then becomes illuminated, as a reminder to the signalman as to which destination button he has operated. Each position of the rotary switch corresponds to one of the five alternative routes from signal number 57 to Platform 7. The rotary switch may have been in any one of its five positions when the signalman pressed the destination button; say it was in position '3', then if the particular route to Platform 7 as selected by position '3' of the selector switch is available, i.e. the interlocking is free, then this particular route will be indicated as being 'available' by a row of magenta-coloured lights on the track diagram. If, however, the route is not 'available', no indication will be given and the signalman will move the rotary switch to further positions to see if any of the remaining alternative routes are available. Having placed the rotary switch in a position which indicates a suitable route available on the diagram, he will leave the switch in that position and then set the route and clear the signal by reversing the main or shunt signal thumb-switch as required. It should be noted that until this thumb-switch is reversed, no interlocking is operated. To restore the route to normal it is only necessary to replace the thumb-switch.

The magenta lights only indicate that a route is free, and of course that would mean free to be set for a movement in either direction. The route used as an example in the foregoing description leads into the station, and if in fact it was set up this would be indicated on the illuminated diagram by the magenta lights changing to amber. If instead a route had been set over the same course for a train to come out of the station, the magenta lights would have changed to lunar white. The miniature lamp unit displaying, as required, any one of three colours through the same aperture, set some pretty little problems in design and manufacture of which I have the most vivid personal recollections!

In the North Eastern Region, where the signalling of the north main line from Newcastle to Burnmouth, just north of the Border, provided a major task, the engineers and operating men postulated a new philosophy towards the design of control panels. Hitherto, as exemplified in the large plants at York and Newcastle, which had been followed in general design in some of the first panel boxes installed on other regions such as Chislehurst, Glasgow Central, and on the London Midland line between Crewe and Manchester referred to later, the operating console had been backed by a vertical illuminated diagram. It had not been considered necessary for the signalmen to see any trains at all, since their progress could be watched on the illuminated diagram, and their class and destination announced by train description. The North Eastern had been a pioneer in panel working, and generally their lead had been followed in the first phase of modernization. Nevertheless, the panel boxes so far installed on the North Eastern had nearly been located at large centres of traffic where there would be station staff and inspectors to see the passage of trains. It was another matter when consideration came to be given to panel boxes in outlying parts controlling thirty or forty miles of open line on which nearly every station was due for closing.

The wheel began to go full circle, and the need was expressed for a control panel box from which the signalman could once again see the trains. It was not considered desirable for him to sit with his back to the line. He should be able to sit at his panel, surveying the running over a wide area as indicated by the lights on the diagram, and be able to see the trains passing his box without getting up or indeed altering his position. In other words, he must see them over the top of his panel. It was appreciated that continuous track circuiting, with the associated indications on the illuminated diagram portion of the panel, obviated the need for a signalman to observe the tail lamps of passing trains; but there are other things to observe, such as shifted loads, hot boxes, tarpaulins coming adrift, and this argument becomes even more cogent now that brake vans on freight trains are being eliminated, and guards are riding on the locomotives. Reverting to the panels themselves, however, it needed no more than the roughest of sketches to show that the use of existing thumb-switches, lamp units and suchlike would not give the desired results. Small though they were in comparison with the parts of the power interlocking frames that had preceded them, they were not small enough for future requirements. Much experience had been gained however over the design of the special coloured-light indicators for the Glasgow Central panel, and this pointed the way. One of the first results of this new approach to panel design was the interlocking at Tweedmouth Junction, which controlled the North Eastern main line from Burnmouth, through Berwick-upon-Tweed, and for some twenty miles to the south. The signalman, without rising from his chair, can operate all the push-buttons needed for regulating traffic in this wide area, and at the same time see the entire sweep of the line itself from Tweedmouth to the Royal Border Bridge and the entry to Berwick station.

Making now a further transition from north-east to south-west of the country, the Western Region approach to modernization embodied yet another feature, new to British practice, in its control panel interlockings. Close study had been made of developing trends on the continent of Europe, where in both Germany and Switzerland the unit or 'domino' principle of panel construction was rapidly becoming standard. The illuminated diagram layout of the most complicated station is built up from a series of standard 'dominoes', representing items such as a single pair of points, a colour-light signal, a diamond crossing, and so on. Each has its operating member in the form of a push-button incorporated in the domino and the miniature electrical gear mounted on the back. The advantage claimed for this principle is that panels can be constructed on a standard framework, and that — more important still! — alterations can be made easily, such as the adding of a signal, removal of a switch connection, and so on. The German version included a rectangular 'domino'; the Swiss version was square. I visited the works of the Integra company in Zurich in 1957, and was fascinated by the practical manner in which these important precepts were being exploited. A. W. Woodbridge, then Signal Engineer of the Western Region, decided to standardize on the domino form of panel for all future power interlockings on the lines of the former Great Western Railway, and during the early stages of the Modernization Plan some large panels were installed at Birmingham Snow Hill, Newport High Street, and in the new Hump marshalling yard at Margam, near Port Talbot.

While the interlocking machine, in whatever form it takes, is necessarily the showpiece of any signalling installation, the rapid developments in control methods, that made possible the extension of the controlled area to the extent exemplified by installations like that at Tweedmouth, constitute the major break-through of the era. This was to be demonstrated in most spectacular form in the later phases of the London Midland Region, to which special reference is made in a separate chapter. The science of electronics was introduced on a limited scale in the early stages of the Modernization Plan, and it quickly revolutionized the whole outlook on the subject of remote control. Mention has been made in Chapter XI of the system of coded remote control developed in the USA and known generally as C.T.C. Its limitations, so far as heavily worked lines are concerned, was the time taken for the codes to be sent and received; but when the electro-magnetic relays in the chain of interlocking controls were replaced by electronic transistors there came a sensational speed-up in transmission. From the situation wherein one code took, at the very fastest, about one and a half seconds to be transacted, the rate increased to something like forty codes per second. With such a 'tool' as high-speed transistorized remote control, the geographical extent of an inter-locking could be as large as convenient, no matter how busy junc-tions at its farthest extremities might be. An example of this was the station and goods yard at Berwick-upon-Tweed, remotely con-trolled from Tweedmouth Junction, some two miles away. This, however, was merely a beginning.

So far in this chapter I have made no more than a passing men-tion of the London Midland Region, where in connection with the great electrification programme the works were the most extensive of any in Great Britain at that time. The subject is indeed large enough to require a separate chapter.

CHAPTER XIV

Re-signalling an Entire Railway

The electrification of the London Midland main line from Euston to Birmingham, Crewe, Liverpool and Manchester has been described as virtually building a new railway over the tracks of an old one. The road-bed had to be renewed throughout; track had to be relaid, and continuously welded for hundreds of miles; stations had to be reconstructed, track layouts streamlined, and in many locations bridges had to be rebuilt. In view of the high capital cost of electrification, it was essential that once completed the utmost use should be made of the new line, even to the extent of re-routing other long-established traffic flows so that as high a mileage as possible should be covered 'under the wires'—as the expression now stands. Accordingly a traffic requirement was laid down that throughout the electrified area an average 'green' headway of four to five minutes should be provided, and in actual practice this meant headways of between two and a half and three and a half minutes for the faster trains. There was the intention to exploit the advantages of electrification to the utmost by scheduling high end-to-end average speeds that would involve continuous running at 90-100 m.p.h. on many sections of the line. At the same time these tracks would also be used by trains running in the 50-60 m.p.h. range, namely, multiple-unit passenger and fitted freights, and at other times by loose-coupled freight trains which, because of their limited brake power, would not run at speeds greatly exceeding 25 m.p.h.

The advantages of modern colour-light signalling, in providing better headway and regulation facilities for all classes of traffic, have already been discussed at length in this book, but it is worth emphasizing that they are in a way complementary to the advantages of electrification itself. But where the system of traction involves overhead structures, there is another reason for the installation of colour-light signalling throughout. Experience elsewhere with electric traction using overhead structures has shown that it is difficult to provide reasonable sighting of a semaphore signal amid the complication of the many supports for overhead traction wires, especially where speeds considerably in excess of 60 m.p.h. are involved. Furthermore, although the electrified area of the London Midland region boasts one of the finest alignments in any part of British Railways, very few stretches are absolutely straight, and with overhead traction wires the incidence of curves greatly impedes the sighting of semaphore signals. Thus it was decided to replace semaphores on running lines throughout the electrified area. The use of colour-light signals, and the desirability of taking full advantage of them for providing good headway facilities for all classes of traffic, made it necessary to space the colour-light signals regularly without relation to the positions of existing block posts, stations or junctions; and as a result of this it was necessary to abolish block working altogether and with it all its limitations, and to provide for track circuiting throughout.

Having decided upon the use of four-aspect colour-light signalling throughout, for the varying reasons just mentioned, it did not necessarily follow that the actual control would have to be from power signal-boxes in all cases; and the planning of the signalling project as a whole, throughout the electrified lines, involved the use of power boxes in certain places and electro-mechanical boxes in others depending upon local conditions. It is, however, important to appreciate that every single mile of the railway was subject to modernization. There was no improvization in order to use existing signals. Everything was reconsidered with regard to the overall pattern of modernization and, although the controls vary in different areas, the aspects displayed to the driver are uniform throughout.

The problem of immunizing signalling apparatus from the effects of stray a.c. traction currents has already been mentioned. In actual practice it was not possible to establish a completely uniform method of dealing with this particular problem, as local conditions varied considerably. One of the main factors with which the electric traction engineers had to deal was the need to obviate, as far as possible, interference with GPO circuits where they are adjacent to the electrified lines. On the traction catenary system, various measures were therefore applied to suppress interference at its source. On the Crewe – Manchester line, for example, booster transformers with rail returns were provided. As the project continued other methods were used on different parts of the line, and south of Crewe three different methods of suppression are being used in various areas to meet the requirements of the Post Office. The varying suppression methods of the traction engineers required varying measures of immunization of the signalling apparatus.

The task has been made more complicated because in addition to the 25-kV 50-cycle traction system, there were other electrical factors liable to cause interference. At Manchester Piccadilly, for example, the electrified lines of the former L.N.E.R. are equipped with the 1,500-volt d.c. traction system using overhead wires. Again at Crewe special measures had to be taken, because at that station a.c. track circuits had previously been provided to combat certain section stray d.c. earth potentials. Quite a different problem was presented in the London suburban area, because the whole line between Euston and Watford is alongside the 630-volt d.c. fourth-rail traction system, immediately adjacent to the new 25-kV lines, and eventually using the same tracks between Camden and Euston.

Turning now to some details of the work, the Manchester – Crewe line was of outstanding interest in that it provided the first example in this country of an entire railway completely re-signalled under one co-ordinated scheme, and brought into service in a series of change-over works, carried out in rapid succession. It was not the first line in this country that has eventually been re-signalled completely from end to end; but in the past the examples that can be found of completely re-signalled railways have usually been carried through in a series of steps extending in some cases over many years, and embodying change in policy and technique before the final stages of the entire installation were brought into service. Between Manchester and Crewe the work was planned as a whole. Leaving out of consideration the Stockport area, the line between Manchester and Crewe, via Styal, was designed to have only two intermediate signal-boxes, namely at Wilmslow and Sandbach.

New relay interlocking control panels were planned for Manchester Piccadilly, Wilmslow, and Sandbach on the Westinghouse O.C.S. system, and the existing all-electric lever interlocking at Crewe was modified to provide immunization from interference by a.c. traction current. The scheme of signalling control and concentration at only two points intermediately between Manchester and Crewe had to take account of the fact that there is a considerable amount of local passenger traffic on this line. Unlike many other sections of British Railways in process of modernization, no intermediate passenger stations were to be closed, and while it was desired, for the purpose of efficient co-ordination of traffic, to concentrate signalling control at no more than a few points, provision had to be made for local working at the intermediate stations when shunting or other subsidiary movements were required. It has already been mentioned that control of what might be termed satellite interlockings was arranged by remote control methods; it is, however, important to appreciate to what extent the work at Wilmslow and Sandbach constituted a piece of pioneer signal engineering. Remote control using relay methods has been well tried in many parts of the world, but, as mentioned in the previous chapter, the use of electronic methods of switching was relatively new, and in no more than an advanced stage of development by the manufacturers. If remote control was to be adopted on a busy line, nothing short of electronic methods would have sufficed; but it needed a great deal of courage on the part of the signal engineers of the London Midland Region to adopt the new system. Their confidence in it, however, was well placed. To indicate the manner in which the principles of remote control have been applied, it will be convenient to refer to Sandbach signal-box in particular. In addition to the functions controlled by direct wire from the Sandbach console, there are four satellite interlockings, at Sydney Bridge, Rookery Bridge, Holmes Chapel and Goostrey, for each of which the apparatus is contained in small buildings at the sites concerned. These satellite interlockings, which are self-contained and include all the usual safety features for operation and interlocking of all the points and signals concerned, differ from an ordinary small signal-box in that there is no individual lever frame or control console. Instead electronic coding equipment is provided whereby the control of these satellite interlockings is effected from the Sandbach console. Similar remote control methods are employed for the satellite interlockings associated with the panels at Wilmslow and Manchester Piccadilly.

In view of the later developments in signalling subsequently described, the panels on the Manchester – Crewe line represent an important stage in the ceaseless process of evolution in signalling practice, but nevertheless include one feature that was novel at the time of its installation, namely, the digital type of indicators for train description. The abolition of the conventional form of block working in consequence of the use of continuous multi-aspect colour-light signalling, necessitated some form of train description and in former years it was no more than natural that the information provided corresponded closely to that given by the bell codes associated with the block system. In other words the signalman was advised of the class of train, and in certain cases also its route. In large interlockings such as York the visual indicators providing this information for signalmen, and relating to the many running lines converging upon the station, were large and complicated.

The adoption of a standard code of train numbering on British Railways, and the carrying of the reporting number on the locomotive or leading vehicle of each train, made possible the development of a much improved system of train description, in which the signalman was advised of the actual timetable reporting number of the train approaching. The compactness of the modern illuminated digital indicator enabled these latter to be mounted on the illuminated diagram, instead of on a separate panel, and by fitting one of these indicators at each signal where there was a telephone the signalman has an 'up-to-the-minute' picture, on his diagram, of the whereabouts of every train; and by watching the changing indications as its number progresses from one signal location to the next he can form a very good impression of the speed of its approach.

The interlockings at Sandbach and Wilmslow are both large, as will be appreciated from the following numerical statistics:

	Sandbach	Wilmslow
Route miles	12	14
Single track miles	28	31
Number of controlled signals	12	13
Number of controlled/automatic signals	23	27
Automatic and semi/automatic signals	16	11
Number of elevated subsidiary signals	10	14
Number of ground signals	13	33
Total number of signalled routes	91	111
Number of point ends that are power-worked	52	61
Number of track circuits indicated on diagram	158	142

141

In sheer size, though identical in principle, these two interlockings are completely dwarfed by the very large one at Manchester Piccadilly. In the route miles controlled it is the smallest of the three, accounting for no more than eleven miles; but the single-track mileage in the approach to this large terminal station is far greater and the layout is infinitely more complicated so far as point and crossing work is concerned. This is reflected in the number of controlled signals—seventy-eight—and the total of elevated subsidiary and ground signals which together amount to 116 units. The total number of signalled routes is the third largest in the entire electrification project, namely 408, and is exceeded only by the interlockings at Rugby and Euston. At Manchester the number of indicated track circuits is 271.

In keeping with the general motif of modernization the new signal-boxes at Sandbach, Wilmslow, and Manchester Piccadilly are of striking design with an exterior colour scheme of pastel blue and white. Some habitués of the line, and some local residents whose tastes were concentrated in the conventional, found these new designs a little too startling for their liking, and at Wilmslow in particular there were local protests as the box structure was built up to what were considered to be unprecedented heights. But protest changed to warm appreciation when the electric service was introduced and regular travellers were able to enjoy the benefits of the much faster and undelayed service that was soon smoothly in operation with the new trains.

The work on the Manchester – Crewe line, and particularly on the section between Wilmslow and Slade Lane Junction via Styal, was a pilot scheme for practically every facet of the electrification scheme. I have already described how the principles of route-relay interlocking that were developed in years before World War II elsewhere in Great Britain were used with very little adaptation in the new signal-boxes at Sandbach, Wilmslow and Manchester Piccadilly. But there was also the important additional technique of using electronic remote-control methods to supervise the working at a number of satellite interlockings. The principle established here was a very important one, and it has been developed to a remarkable extent in the later stages of the modernization scheme as a whole. For a variety of reasons, however, it was not possible to do this on the Liverpool line, although there is one notable advance to be recorded in this latter case. But in the Black Country, and at Rugby and points south, the principle of remote control was exploited to an extent unprecedented so far as British main-line traffic is concerned. One of the most interesting features incorporated in the power signal-boxes on the Manchester – Crewe line, as previously mentioned, was the incorporation of digital indicators, displaying the reporting number of the trains concerned, at every signal location on the illuminated diagrams. The diagrams themselves were of the older type used in previous route-relay interlockings elsewhere in this country, and although they and the associated control consoles represented a very considerable reduction in size over the machines that would have been required had a lever interlocking with electric interlocking between levers been used, the diagrams and the operating units on the control console would now be regarded as quite large. To take full advantage of the principles of electronic remote control, and bring really extensive sections of railway under the direct supervision of a single control instrument, further miniaturization was desirable. The facility of having the reporting number of the trains displayed on the actual diagram, through the agency of the train describer apparatus, was considered so great an advantage that the miniaturization process had to apply to the digital indicators as much as to all the rest of the equipment concerned.

The first fruits of the miniaturization process in the London Midland electrification scheme was to be seen in the control panel installed at Edge Hill. It was certainly a bold piece of signal engineering planning to provide a control machine to be worked by only one man, capable of dealing with passenger traffic on the Liverpool to Manchester main line, with the electrified line towards Runcorn and Crewe, with the very heavy freight traffic originating in the Liverpool docks and sorted in the historic Gridiron Marshalling Yard, and also with the special passenger traffic workings that occur on occasions in connection with ocean liner traffic and from Riverside Station. It is always difficult to make direct comparison between one interlocking area and another, but for comparative purposes so far as the size of the control instrument was concerned, whereas the instrument and illuminated diagram for Wilmslow had an overall length of some twenty-three feet, the combined switch panel and diagram for Edge Hill had an overall length of no more than thirteen feet. The track layout and the intensity of train working is infinitely greater at Edge Hill.

Although both interlockings involve route switching, the methods of operation at Edge Hill are different from those on the Manchester line, and Edge Hill has, in general, set the pattern for future installations on the London Midland Region. On the Manchester line the interlockings were of the one-control switch type (O.C.S.). In this system, on the control console each signal has a group of switches associated with it, one switch relating to each of the various alternative routes that are possible from that signal. At a simple junction there would be only two switches, one for each route; but in the approaches to a busy station it can well be appreciated that there would be many switches for many of the signals, and some of these signals would provide for shunt movements as well as running movements. The shunting movements would have to have separate switches.

In the great majority of its applications this form of interlocking definitely requires a separate console. It would be unpractical to mount groups of switches on an illuminated diagram in their correct geographical position to the signals concerned. This has been done in certain installations of a relatively simple kind, but in a layout of the complexity of Edge Hill so much space would be taken on the diagram as to defeat the whole object of miniaturization in other respects. The system of working at Edge Hill is therefore arranged on the 'entrance-exit' principle in which a signalman has to operate two functions in order to set up a route. He is required to press a button at the point of commencement of the route and then to select the appropriate button at the termination of that route as shown on the diagram. These buttons are placed in the correct geographical positions on the tracks and by miniaturizing the design of the switch, of which the button forms an integral part, a very neat and compact layout is achieved.

While a great deal of attention has been paid to making the control machines as compact as possible, and by eliminating all physical work enabling the signalmen to exercise to the full their functions as regulators of the flow of traffic, the associated electrical equipment 'downstairs', and the wiring that goes with it has become very much more elaborate and extensive. To anyone who visits a modern signal-box and is shown the relay-room it might

Electro-pneumatic point layout (with covers removed) on Manchester – Crewe line near Wilmslow

GROUND GEAR TODAY

The first London Transport chair-lock layout on the District line, at Earls Court

THE EARLS COURT CONTROL-ROOM, LONDON TRANSPORT

54. From this equipment surveillance and control of all traffic between South Kensington and Acton Town is effected through programme machines

A CLASSIC CONTROL-TOWER LAYOUT

55. Tees Yard, Middlesbrough, Eastern Region

well seem that the complications are getting so great as to provide an absolute nightmare for those responsible for maintenance. The secret of efficient maintenance is, of course, the clear and effective labelling of all the connections; but in recent years it has been felt that labelling was not enough. Wiring, whether in the actual scheming out of the circuits or in the carrying out of the work on site and the subsequent testing, is a lengthy process, and much consideration has been given towards its simplification.

To some extent the trend of modern railway development in Great Britain, and particularly on the electrified lines of the London Midland, is proving of considerable assistance to this end. Many connections and sidings formerly used have been dispensed with, the general speeding up of traffic with electric locomotives is making the provision of running loops and refuge sidings unnecessary, and consequently the layout of the line itself is becoming a great deal simpler. Track layouts at intermediate points are tending to contain less that is special to a particular locality and with the development of modern signalling practice one could say that the electrical equipment and circuits for doing certain things, such as operating a pair of points or a cross-over, are becoming standardized.

The principle was thus evolved that the units concerned with the control and operation of a certain function would be grouped together in the relay-rooms as units in themselves, with standard wiring, pre-wired before installation and treated all the time as a group rather than individual items of electrical equipment. An interlocking designed in this way thus consists of a certain number of standard unit groups, connected to each other by standard cables. In such an installation, however, local conditions may not permit of the exclusive use of standard units, and additional relays and so on have to be used, and connected to the standard units by what is sometimes termed 'free-wiring', according to the geographical relation of the various points and signals in the station or junction concerned. This principle is nowadays known by the general term 'geographical circuitry'.

The principle of having a central interlocking at major traffic centres, and a number of satellite interlockings electronically remote-controlled from the main box, has been applied to a most spectacular extent on the southern part of the main line. A few years ago, if it had been suggested that one could travel over the 113 miles from Birmingham New Street to Euston under the control successively of no more than seven signal-boxes, such a suggestion might well have seemed a flight of fancy, rather than a piece of practical railway engineering and operation. It is certainly true that technically there was no limit to which signalling controls could be concentrated; but so many practical points intervened between the ideal of highly concentrated control at a few points and its practical achievement, that there would have been a tendency to lay such thoughts on one side. But the success attending the introduction of electronic remote-control methods made such a proposition a very successful actuality. Those seven boxes are now Birmingham, Coventry, Rugby, Bletchley, Watford, Willesden and Euston.

So far as route miles are concerned, pride of place goes easily to the new installation at Rugby, which controls no less than fifty-nine miles. The area involved extends in the north to the outskirts of Nuneaton on the one hand, and Coventry on the other, and, in the south, throughout the main line to the approaches of Wolverton. On the Northampton loop-line the immediate area of Northampton itself remains electro-mechanically controlled. Geographically the position of Northampton in relation to the main line via Weedon has some interesting points of resemblance to that of Stockport in relation to the Styal line. The difference is, however, that whereas in the case of Stockport there was one interlocking at the northern end of the area, at Manchester Piccadilly, and another interlocking at the southern end at Wilmslow, in the case of the Rugby and Northampton area the junctions at the southern end, at Roade, are supervised from Rugby. In the case of the Styal line there was a separate signal-box at Wilmslow.

In making this comparison, of course, I am quite aware that Manchester Piccadilly handles a far more intense local traffic than that dealt with at Rugby, and that there probably would have been difficulty in extending remote control from Manchester to include Wilmslow. Furthermore, when these two latter installations were put into commission one would very much doubt if the engineering and operating officers would have been ready to accept such a wide extension of electronic remote control. What has been done from

Rugby is significant of the confidence that has been bred in the systems by the earlier experience in the north.

Continuing on the main line towards London there are three further power interlockings, each with a group of satellites: one at Bletchley, one at Watford Junction and one at Willesden. In these cases the signal-boxes are placed at the points of major interlocking, and the satellites are relatively simple layouts. The main line is continuously quadruple-tracked over the last sixty miles from Roade into London, and the satellite interlockings are most concerned with the provision of cross-over facilities from fast to slow roads and *vice versa*, and with occasional shunting facilities for pick-up and setting down of local goods traffic.

Apart from the layout of signals at the major interlockings, providing for shunt movements, cross-overs and suchlike on the open stretches of line, the layout of the signals had to cater for three major sets of conditions: one, provision for the running of high-speed express passenger trains continuously at 90-100 m.p.h.; two, to provide for the running of multiple-unit passenger trains and fitted freight trains at 50-60 m.p.h.; and, three, to provide for the 35-m.p.h. unfitted freights. The signalling system had to cater for all classes of traffic, to enable them to run at close headways where required, and at the same time to have adequate braking distance from their maximum running speeds. These three differing sets of conditions provide an extremely good example of the effectiveness of four-aspect colour-light signals in modern railway conditions. The average spacing of the signals on the open stretches is about 1,200 yards, which means that from passing signals displaying the double-yellow indication the distance to the red is 2,400 yards. This provides adequate braking distance for express passenger trains travelling at 100 m.p.h. On the other hand, the multiple-unit passenger trains and the fitted freights do not need so great a braking distance when travelling at their maximum speed of 60 m.p.h. and they could, if necessary, take the double yellow as their 'all-clear' and only apply the brakes to reduce speed when a single yellow is sighted. The use of four-aspect colour-light signals, therefore, permits both classes of train—the 100-m.p.h. express passenger trains, and the 60-m.p.h. fitted freights—to run at relatively close headway with safe braking distance from their maximum speeds.

The signalling at Euston has always been subject to very great interest among railwaymen because of the historic nature of the station itself. It is not one of the largest interlockings on the electrified London Midland lines, nor does it cover a very large route mileage. But in the complexity and intensity of the working in the synthesis of high-speed main-line trains, shorter-distance a.c. electric, the d.c. electrics, and the very heavy parcel traffic, it provides one of the busiest interlockings to be found anywhere on the London Midland Region. The last two phases leading up to the present reconstruction may be briefly recalled. In the days of the London and North Western Railway, the signalling in the immediate approaches to the terminus was a mixture of standard London and North Western Railway mechanical working and the Crewe all-electric system of power operation. The change to colour-light signalling, in 1952, was occasioned by the urgent need to lengthen six of the platforms and at the same time to equip the station area with track circuiting throughout. Three of the platforms scheduled for attention were the principal arrival lines, Nos. 1 2 and 3, and the old No. 2 mechanical box occupied such a large area on the ground as to prove an obstacle to the lengthening of these platforms.

This box, which was situated almost beneath the No. 4 bridge, controlled the running movements throughout the immediate approaches to the station. It was a large interlocking, with 288 mechanical levers arranged in two rows, so that the signalmen in each group were working back to back with their opposite numbers. So far as the present reconstruction is concerned, history is to some extent repeating itself. In 1952, the old No. 2 signal-box had got to be removed to make the necessary space; in 1964 it was the No. 4 bridge itself that had got to go, because its piers were blocking the way for the permanent way modernization needed. When the station was changed over to colour-light signalling in 1952, a miniature 227-lever frame with all-electric interlocking was installed in a new box situated on the up side of the line immediately to the north of Hampstead Road Bridge.

The new miniaturized route-relay interlocking is designed on the 'entrance-exit' principle, as at Liverpool Edge Hill, and it controls the largest number of routes of any interlocking in the entire resignalling of the London Midland main line. Whereas Manchester Piccadilly has 408 signalled routes, and the very extensive Rugby interlocking has 467, Euston has 1,554 routes which is, of course, a clear indication of the complexity of the layout and the complications of the traffic. Its geographical extent, covered only as far as the eastern end of Primrose Hill tunnel, is not great and in fact covers only three route miles. In that area, however, there are no less than 200 indicated track circuits on the illuminated diagrams, as compared with 271 in the eleven route miles of Manchester Piccadilly. The control-room together with the associated relay-rooms is accommodated in a large building to the west of the station on the site formerly occupied by a small engine yard, immediately to the west of No. 15 platform line. The area controlled by the box covers all the main running lines from Primrose Hill Tunnel into the terminus, and the system of interconnecting fly-over and burrowing junctions on Camden Bank by which engine and empty carriage movements are kept clear of main-line running movements.

The work in the Black Country in sheer magnitude was perhaps even more spectacular than at Euston, with only three main-line signal-boxes controlling the running over the whole of the former L.N.W.R. lines in the Birmingham – Walsall – Wolverhampton complex. The panel interlocking at New Street, built on similar principles to those at Edge Hill and Euston, is one of the largest single interlocking plants put into service anywhere in the world, though it will soon be closely paralleled by the installations now in process of erection on the former Midland line, with large panel boxes at Saltley, Derby and Trent. These latter of course lie outside the present electrified area, but their design was based directly upon the experience gained with the North Western installations. Lastly among the large panel boxes on the electrified railway is Stoke-on-Trent, providing the major North Staffordshire contribution to the general signal modernization.

CHAPTER XV

Modern Practice on London's Underground

The first steps towards a series of quite revolutionary developments in signalling practice on London Transport railways, all the inventions of Mr Robert Dell, were taken more than twenty-five years ago with the introduction of the 'power-worked-lever remote-control system'. The development of relay interlocking, and remote-control methods on the main-line railways of Great Britain and elsewhere had been studied carefully to see to what extent similar methods could be applied on the railways of London Transport. In many respects the operating conditions were different, having regard to the overriding need for clearing any faults with the utmost promptitude. The consequences of prolonged hold-up on a 'tube' railway are all too obvious. It was felt that with existing systems of relay interlocking there would, in the conditions obtaining on London Transport, be greater difficulty in handling traffic while a failure was being located. So, Dell set out to obtain the undoubted advantages of remote control and route working, while retaining interlocking of the normal type.

Until the introduction of the first remotely controlled interlocking frames London Transport, while employing lever frames of similar appearance to those in use elsewhere, had always retained mechanical interlocking between the levers. The installations themselves were individually small, and the routes simple. The lever interlocking was correspondingly simple, and on this reckoning alone perhaps more desirable than all-electric interlocking. In providing for the remote control of complete interlockings Robert Dell retained all the standard features of his existing frames, with the usual back-locks and track-locks on the levers, and with full track circuit control of the signals; but the levers themselves were arranged to be moved by two small compressed-air cylinders, one for normal, one for reverse, governed by electro-pneumatic valves attached to each cylinder. The control of the movement of the levers was effected from a distant point. The arrangement included individual levers for each signal or pair of points, but the control of the lever movements could be devised so that the operation of a single thumb-switch would operate all the levers required to set up a complete route. In so doing, however, a very important matter of principle was established, that was to form the cornerstone of the still more spectacular developments that followed after the end of World War II. That principle was the making of a clear distinction between 'safety' and 'non-safety' circuits.

The safety circuits are those controlling the functioning of signals and points, as regulated by the movement of levers in the interlocking frame. The latter is safeguarded by the mechanical interlocking, the back-locks and track-locks, and the track circuit control of the signals. All these safety features are provided for with standard, well-tried railway signalling apparatus. The circuits for remote control of the lever operation, which had no effect on the safe operation of the signalling, were non-safety. In a normal interlocking frame, if it is unsafe for the signalman to pull a certain lever it is mechanically or electrically locked, and he is prevented from attempting to make such a movement. It was just the same on the remotely controlled frame. If the lever was locked, no manipulation of the distant control would move it. The non-safety circuits could thus be wired and equipped with cheap mass-produced telephone-type apparatus, thus saving cost and space.

For London Transport conditions Dell claimed that the advantages of the system were:

1. The location of faults by the lineman is greatly simplified. By an inspection of the position of the levers in the interlocking frame it can be quickly determined whether a defect is on the signal control circuit or on the operation circuit. It is simple and straightforward and a defect in one circuit does not affect other signal or points circuits.

2. The handling of traffic movements while the fault is being corrected is greatly facilitated, as one of the traffic staff can operate the levers at the interlocking frame, should the fault be on the operation circuits.

3. The cost can be lower than for a single large interlocking frame controlling a large layout, as the small interlocking frames can be placed close to the signals operated and the expensive signalling cables be kept short.

4. The signalling is less vulnerable to damage by fire or other causes, in consequence of the dispersal of the signalling equipment among a number of small signal-boxes and relay-rooms.

5. Alterations are easier to carry out, because it is probable that work will be restricted to one signal-box and there is not the likelihood of work in progress inadvertently affecting other parts of the system, as may happen when work had to be done in a large relay-room.

In stressing the advantage of dispersal of the equipment among a number of small signal-boxes and relay-rooms, he was no doubt thinking of wartime conditions. Nevertheless he was not alone in expressing some uneasiness of the risk of building such huge concentrations of signalling equipment as the tendencies in the immediate pre-war years had shown. His own system went some way towards providing the best of both worlds, with the normal functioning of a large centralized control, and the facility of working any of the satellites individually in case of emergency. I appreciate that the recording of this London Transport development of the early 1940s comes out of strict chronological sequence, having been discussing the electronic remote-control installations of the 1960s on the London Midland Region in the previous chapter. But the work on London Transport must be considered as something apart, and the power-worked-lever remote-control system formed the first step in a continuous chain of development leading to the signalling of the fully-automated Victoria Line tube, brought into service in 1968.

Robert Dell, as much as any railway engineer of the day, was aware of the immense advantages in operation to be derived from centralized control; and in the strictly ordered movements of multiple-unit trains on the Underground lines, completely unimpeded on the 'tube' routes by extraneous shunting, goods trains, light-engine movements and other factors that in other circumstances can cause dislocation and delay, he had a framework on which to build a new conception of automatic signalling, that included automatic working of junctions as well.

For the most part junction layouts on the London Transport lines are simple, and provide for through running without the complication of shunting or other accompaniments which are features of main-line railway practice. To provide for automatic working of junctions three methods are available. All passengers are familiar with the train destination indicators on the District, Metropolitan, and certain of the tube lines, where trains using a common track in the central area such as the Circle lines between Mansion House and Sloane Square run to a variety of destinations in outer London. The routing of these trains onto their various diverging tracks begins at South Kensington with the segregation of the Circle trains, and it continues at Earls Court (for Wimbledon), Turnham Green (for Richmond) and Acton Town. It is possible so to arrange the train description circuits that they can control the operation of the facing points at diverging junctions, and thus obviate any need for signalmen to operate the points for successive trains. At trailing junctions where two routes are converging, automatic operation of points can be very simply arranged on the 'first come, first served' principle. Neither the automatic setting of facing points according to the train description nor the 'first come, first served' principle is entirely satisfactory, because the service is not necessarily kept in timetable order, and a very small lateness or earlyness at a converging junction could result in trains being run out of order. Furthermore it is not easy to originate the running of a train, that is to say, the systems could not provide for the starting up of a train from a siding or from a terminus. Lastly there is the great disadvantage that with either of these methods one cannot exercise a time control on train movements.

It was to surmount these difficulties and to provide fully automatic working of junctions that the system of programme machine working was devised. The 'programme' embodies full details of the train service for an entire day. It is in the form of a roll of plastic film eight inches wide, with holes punched in one line across it to provide the information for each train. In substance it is similar to the paper roll used on a player-piano, or in modern business machinery equipment on a punched tape. The programme machines are designed to accommodate rolls of a maximum length of about forty feet and these can carry information for about 1,200 trains. Provision is made for the total of thirty-two holes to be punched on the line relative to each train, so that a very large amount of information can be provided. This is important because it enables the controlling circuits to be greatly simplified.

In addition to carrying full details of the train service for a day, and in consequence being able to set the routes over a junction from this information in timetable order, the programme machine can also carry out the following functions:

1. It carries the full details of the train service for a day and can set the routes over a junction from this information, in timetable order.

2. In conjunction with a second machine, it can check the time of each train, and as a result:
   (a) Sound an alarm if a train is late by more than a predetermined time,
   (b) Delay the clearing of a signal until it is time for the train to depart.

3. Check the correct operation of the train describer.

4. When a train is originated by the machine, such as starting it out of a siding, to transmit the destination on the train describer.

5. In conjunction with the electrical circuits, to signal a waiting train out of turn, if the train scheduled to run before it is late by more than a predetermined amount, and to store the information that this has been done, routing the late train as soon as it arrives.

The rolls are driven by a small electric motor and photo-cells control the movement of the roll from one line of holes to another. The control of the driving motor is initiated by the actual movements of the trains themselves over successive track circuits. At the operation of a track circuit the motor is started and the forward clutch energized. The motor then drives the roll forward until another row of holes is brought into line, at which time the special hole in front of the forward photo-cell lines up and this cuts off the drive to the motor and applies the brakes. The reading of the holes punched on the programme roll is by means of a series of feelers, the twin contacts of which are closed when the feeler enters a hole in the roll. It will be appreciated that with a maximum capacity of thirty holes and thirty feelers a large number of contact combinations is available for setting up of circuits for operation of points at the junctions concerned.

Programme machine working is being applied stage by stage to the whole of the London Transport electric railway network. One of the earliest applications was on the Northern Line, at the junctions of Camden Town and Kennington, and over the two alternative routes connecting these junctions, namely, one via Bank and one via Leicester Square. The junctions at Camden Town and Kennington are now entirely automatically operated, but an essential and very interesting feature of the entire principle of programme machine work is the setting up of central control rooms from which the operation in the entire area concerned can be scrutinized. The central supervision rooms, one of which is at Leicester Square, are similar to a centralized signal control room, and have illuminated diagrams showing the movements of all trains in the area. But whereas the signal control room, in a modern push-button form of interlocking, is a place where the operation of points and the clearing of signals is actually initiated, in the London Transport supervision rooms the men on duty do not have to carry out any signalling as such, as the points are worked automatically by the programme machine. They are there to exercise a supervisory function, or to intervene and exercise manual control if circumstances should make this necessary.

Operation of the actual junction is controlled by an interlocking frame working generally on the same principle as the remote-controlled-lever interlocking frames referred to earlier in this chapter: but to economize in space at locations that are mostly deep underground, a new form of interlocking machine was designed, having a series of vertical shafts, one for each signal or pair of points. Mechanical interlocking is provided between the shafts exactly as in the more conventional type of interlocking, and the signal and points circuits start from contacts on the vertical shaft. The shafts themselves are rotated as required through an angle of 60°, to operate the contacts, by small compressed-air cylinders. The whole assembly is extremely economical in space and provides for the utmost accessibility for maintenance purposes. It is a notable thing that throughout all these highly sophisticated developments on London Transport the basic safety principle of mechanical interlocking between levers has been retained, even though the interlocking frame has taken an entirely new physical form. Another interesting feature of these new interlocking machines, of which I personally have vivid memories, was the new design of interlocking mechanisms. Until the introduction of this form of interlocking machine the construction of the interlocking mechanism had always been based on the assumption that the final working and the integrity of the locking itself depended on hand-fitting of the various locking bars, dogs, and suchlike. The locking fitter in the signal department of a railway, or of a contractor, was a skilled craftsman, and it was partly in the realization of this, with modern signalling practices, and the increasing complication of the interlocking required on large control machines, that many signal engineers had turned to purely electrical methods of achieving the interlocking, thus eliminating the skilled individual work that was always necessary to fit mechanical locking into a frame. Robert Dell conceived the idea that if the various parts of the interlocking mechanism were all manufactured to precision standards, to dimensions mathematically determined beforehand, the mechanism could be *assembled* rather than *fitted*, and that in future the only tools required by a 'locking fitter' would be a screwdriver.

I remember very well hearing one of Mr Dell's most senior assistants speaking at the Institution of Railway Signal Engineers in respect of the programme machine. When Mr Dell read a very comprehensive paper to that Institution in 1958, describing the programme machine installation on the Northern Line, one of the speakers in the discussion was Walter Owen, who had been very deeply concerned with the installation. He said: 'When the idea was first mooted there was a tendency among some of the staff in the London Transport signal engineer's drawing office to throw up their hands in horror and to say: "This is the end. It will never work." But Mr Dell with his persuasive powers got them working on it and the first attempt was at Kennington, where almost to the last day before the opening some still said: "It will never work". But it did!' Listening to Mr Owen on that occasion my thoughts went back several years earlier to the time when Mr Dell had first propounded to us in Westinghouse the idea of an interlocking mechanism that did not require any fitting. I am afraid our reaction was very much the same: 'You just can't do it'. But the story, within our own design and manufacturing organization, anticipated exactly what happened within Mr Dell's own design department at Earls Court over the programme machine. We had no end of a struggle to establish the correct dimensions, and the limits and fits that had got to be laid down; but it was achieved in the end and after the first interlocking machine was built this particular London Transport product became one of those things that were treated as a matter of the simplest routine. I cannot add that the locking fitter became completely extinct in our organization from that time onwards, because there are still overseas railways that require mechanical frames with locking of the conventional type. But from that time onwards no London Transport interlocking machines had any locking fitted to them. Instead the frames were despatched with appropriate quantities of 'dogs', 'cats', and screws, for the London Transport assemblers, who arranged the locking as the various junctions required.

CHAPTER XVI

Marshalling Yards

It has often been said that the signal engineer has got to be a jack of all trades. In recent years this tag has applied with redoubled emphasis to contractors' staffs, and particularly to those concerned with the engineering of modern marshalling yards. The British Railways Modernization Plan included an important section covering the replacement of a great number of small, manually-worked yards by a few large, fully-mechanized layouts, and in this new work the signal engineer had a part of predominating importance to play. The efficient working of a fully mechanized yard is the outcome of the interplay of a series of widely differing factors, the responsibility for which is vested variously in three different engineering departments of the railway, not to mention the traffic; the signal manufacturer is in the delicate position of being adviser as well as contractor to two of those railway engineering departments, and adviser both to the third of this trio, and to the traffic department.

The overall requirement of a marshalling yard is to provide for a certain through-put of wagons every day. The average will not necessarily be in the form of a steady flow hour by hour; there may be certain times in the day when traffic rises to a peak of intensity, while at others there is very little passing through. But however the overall figure is made up, a study of existing business and anticipated trends will show that there will be times in the day when it is necessary to pass X wagons an hour through the yard. Physical conditions very rarely permitted of the building of a new yard on the site of an old one; usually land had to be purchased. This, while making the constructional and change-over work easier, involved greater capital expense. Shunting on the 'hump' principle was taken for granted, and with higher running-speeds of wagons, to obtain the maximum rate of hourly throughput, it was essential to have power operation of points, with some form of automatic control.

In any matter of point operation the signal engineer is immediately involved, but in a mechanized marshalling yard the problems are infinitely more complex than that of merely moving the switches a matter of four and a quarter inches from normal to reverse, or *vice versa*. In ordinary railway working one must wait until the preceding train has cleared the fouling point before attempting to move the points; then one moves them in the confidence that all signals reading over those points are at danger, and will be interlocked so until the point stroke is completed and the detection made. Only then can the appropriate signal be cleared for a train to approach and pass over the points. In a marshalling yard a freight train, having had its wagons uncoupled according to the destination of successive wagons or groups of wagons, is propelled over the hump in one continuous movement, and the points for the various routes have often to be set between successive cuts. To give a certain amount of space the gradient leading from the hump is made quite steep, so that on passing over the crest a wagon runs away quickly and separates out from the succeeding one. But from the technical viewpoint of the signal engineer, there is not a fraction of a second to spare, because there may be a second wagon approaching at 15-20 m.p.h. and not twenty yards away when the points have to be changed. In the best of circumstances the timing is critical, but it is made even more so by various other factors that nearly always intervene.

First of all there are considerable variations in the rolling resistances of wagons—some running much more freely than others. Then, weather conditions can seriously affect the running speeds of wagons travelling 'light' under the influence of gravity. A heavy cross-wind acting on an unladen covered wagon can alter its rolling resistance on that day much more than that of a flat bogie-bolster wagon laden with rails! While the provision of adequate space between cuts is the first consideration in the switching area of the yard, once the last pair of points has been negotiated there is another pertinent factor in the distance available, in that siding before the running 'cut' buffers up with wagons already there. The speed of impact must not be too great otherwise there is a risk of damage to merchandise and wagon, and possibly derailment. If the speed of running is such that the wagon stops short, failing to buffer up at all, time will be wasted afterwards while the humping engine is brought down to propel the wagon up to the limit of the space available.

The civil engineer, in respect of gradients and switching area layout, and the mechanical engineer in respect of the running resistance of the wagons, have to agree on a yard profile that will allow the worst running wagon, in the most adverse of atmospheric conditions, to run from the point of detachment on the hump crest to the furthest extent of any sorting sidings. There can be no compromise over that gradient profile; one has to legislate for the worst —not an average. This basic need immediately brings problems for the signal engineer. Despite the steep initial gradient from the hump, a free-running wagon following a 'worst' could so gain on its predecessor as to lessen the distance between to such an extent that there was insufficient time to operate the points between them. Thus, gradients and rolling resistance are not only the province of the civil and mechanical engineer. The signal engineers must also be called in to advise upon the probable minimum needs of distance between cuts. The position of the first pair of diverging points, known as the 'king' points, is most critical.

With the gradients arranged to provide for the worst runners, it stands to reason that the free runners, if unchecked, would go careering down the yard at altogether excessive speed, with disastrous results in the sorting sidings, if they had not become derailed earlier. It is thus necessary to install retarders, by which the speed of wagons may be carefully regulated.

In so doing one moves into the realm of massive, heavy engineering. Considerable power is necessary to control 'cuts' of wagons with aggregate weights up to 100 tons, or even more, travelling at 15-20 m.p.h. Retarders are the province of the railway chief mechanical engineer; but these operations and control are so bound up with the automatic point setting that it has become traditional for them to be incorporated in the overall scheme of control for the yard, and dealt with by the signalling contractor. The first retarders with which I had any connection were installed at Whitemoor Yard near March L.N.E.R. in 1933, under the direction of Sir Nigel

MARSHALLING YARD SITE FROM THE AIR
Carlisle at an early stage in the construction, looking north to the Solway Firth, which can be seen top left of picture

57.
Leicester Square central control-room

LONDON TRANSPORT SPECIALITIES

58.
New type interlocking machine at Watford Junction, Metropolitan line

Gresley. The science of marshalling yard mechanism was, however, then in its infancy, and the actual control of the retarders was by means of hand-operated control valves, relying entirely on the experience and judgment of the operator.

Experience with the early yards on the L.N.E.R. and with those installed at Toton, near Nottingham on the L.M.S.R., led to the development of highly sophisticated methods for the control of retarders. In the earlier yards wagons passed through only one retarder on their way from the hump to the sorting sidings; but in large modern yards in which there are often fifty or more sorting sidings, it has been found necessary to provide for two stages of retardation, and the control of the degree of retardation applied to each cut is made completely automatic in both the primary and the secondary retarders. After this reference to some of the factors that have to be taken into account in applying automatic control methods, a description of the sites and functions of some of the more important yards commissioned under the British Railways Modernization Plan is desirable. At the same time, one has also the poignant duty of stating that a few of these yards, upon which so much engineering skill was lavished, are already redundant because of the rapidly changing trends of modern railway traffic. They were designed more than ten years ago, when the conveyance of freight in single-wagon consignments was still a major point in the overall strategy of British railway operation. Now the whole trend is to eliminate marshalling altogether, and run 'block-loads' of container 'flats', or other special wagons permanently coupled as a single set train.

While the changing trends have rendered some fully-mechanized yards redundant, one imagines it will still be many years before traffic flows can be so ordered as to eliminate *all* marshalling, and the majority of the great yards installed in the 1958-65 period are likely to have many years of working ahead of them. The location and traffic at four yards may be mentioned particularly, namely:

1. Temple Mills, near Stratford, Eastern Region
2. Kingmoor, Carlisle, London Midland Region
3. Tees, near Middlesbrough, Eastern Region
4. Tyne, near Newcastle, Eastern Region.

Temple Mills lying beside the old Cambridge main line of the Great Eastern, just to the north of Stratford, is a concentration and distributional point for freight from the eastern counties into London. Today all the through passenger traffic from Liverpool Street to the Cambridge line, and to the Enfield and Chingford branches, is routed via Hackney Downs, thus leaving the older and more circuitous route from Liverpool Street to Tottenham and the Cambridge main line as an ideal goods route. This is particularly advantageous as routes to the London Docks originate at Stratford. The setting up of the one large yard at Temple Mills enabled a number of small shunting yards to be closed, and a considerable amount of trip-working between yards eliminated. In the main yard there are forty-seven sorting sidings, and regulating the speed of running in these sidings there are two primary retarders and eight secondary ones. While the yard is primarily concerned with traffic from the north, bound for various destinations in the London area coming in from the Cambridge main line, there are connections into the reception area of the yard from the down line at Temple Mills, though traffic from this direction is not so heavy.

The general situation at Carlisle is different. At Temple Mills the traffic is predominantly in one direction, from the north and East Anglia into London, and there is only one hump yard. The railway geography of Carlisle, with its historic associations extending back to the earliest days of through traffic between England and Scotland, is well known to railway enthusiasts, and even today, forty-five years after the grouping—let alone nationalization—the flows of traffic are much the same as of old. The tendency is to concentrate Anglo-Scottish business on the West Coast route, and there have been threats to close down the Settle and Carlisle section of the former Midland Railway, and the Waverley route of the North British. So far, however, none of these threats have materialized, and one still has the Caledonian, Glasgow and South Western, and North British lines converging on Carlisle from the north. To the south the North Western and the Midland come in as of old, together with the Newcastle line from the east, and the Maryport from the south-west.

Following the general pattern of railway build-up, in pre-grouping days there were a number of separate goods yards; though before the nineteenth century was out the congestion in the Citadel station was such that a large combined scheme for diverting all goods traffic clear of the Citadel station led to the construction of the Dentonholme goods yards, and approach lines from the south that avoided the crossing of conflicting routes on the level. The new scheme, provided for under the British Railways Modernization Plan, involved the construction of two huge new yards between Kingmoor and Gretna, to the west of the main lines, to deal with the marshalling of all freight traffic passing through Carlisle to and from Scotland. The southern entry to the yard is immediately to the north of Kingmoor motive power depot, but on the opposite side of the line. The northern entry is by a 'flyover' from the up main line near Floriston. The new yards are also used by trains to and from the North British 'Waverley' route. The entry to this for passenger trains is at Port Carlisle Junction, about a mile *south* of the southern entry to the new mechanized marshalling yards. Up freight trains off the Waverley route diverge from the latter at Longtown and take the spur to the Caledonian line at Gretna. Down freight trains for the Waverley route marshalled in the new yard are at first drawn southwards to make a trailing connection with the down Waverley line at Canal Junction, whence they go forward.

There are two separate humps, each serving quite distinct groups of sorting sidings. The up yard has eight sidings on the reception side of the hump, and forty-eight sorting sidings. There are two primary retarders and eight secondary retarders leading to the forty-eight sorting sidings. The down yard is not so large and has only thirty-seven sorting sidings. The retarder equipment consists of two primaries and six secondaries. The control of all these retarders is entirely automatic. At Carlisle a special form of signal is used in the reception sidings to indicate when a train standing there is to be humped. These signals differ from the ordinary form of colour-light signal and are of the position-light type developed on the L.M.S.R. for the yards at Toton. Both the up and the down yards have their own control tower and in each tower there are two separate control panels, one controlling the humping of trains and the other the general signalling of traffic. In such a large area, with complexity of movement, it was very important to arrange for the most complete co-ordination of freight train movements with movements to and from the main lines alongside. In addition to the yard towers there is a modern push-button-panel signal-box at

Kingmoor Junction, which controls the entry into the yard from the south.

The Tees yard, which again consists of two sections for up and down traffic, provides yet another example of the co-ordination of signalling and operations in a marshalling yard with traffic flowing on the other lines alongside. The Tees up and down yards are interesting as representing a modernization of the famous North Eastern Railway Erimus Yard, one of the earliest in this country to be laid down on the hump principle and notable for the introduction of the three-cylinder type of locomotive for humping operations. To convert an old yard and produce the fine modern layout involved some extremely intricate stage work on the part of the civil engineers. So far as the mechanization work is concerned, the general layout is similar to that at Carlisle except that it is only the primary retarders that have full automatic control. The secondary retarders, while necessarily being power-operated, are controlled by individual push-button applications to provide adjustments of retarding power based on the experience and judgment of the operators concerned.

The fourth yard for particular mention is located beside the East Coast main line at Lamesley. This was an entirely new development, and provided a parallel to yards like Temple Mills, in East London, and Carlisle, in that it replaced a large number of existing small yards in the Newcastle and south Tyne area. Again one has concentrated into a control tower the panels for both hump yard and ordinary signalling controls; but whereas at Carlisle and Tees yard the signalling merely regulated movements to and from the main line in the immediate vicinity of the yards, at Lamesley the signalling panel controls the East Coast main line from the Gateshead panel to the outskirts of Durham.

The layout and equipment of these four yards provide yet another example of the way in which the sphere of activity of railway signal engineers has broadened during the past thirty years. In the yard at Lamesley, known officially as 'Tyne', one can observe the trend towards the eventual control of all railway operating movements from a single centre, in that a marshalling yard with all its activities is here combined, to all intents and purposes, with fourteen miles of heavily-worked high-speed main lines.

Although it has no direct connection with marshalling yards, reference may also be made at this stage to the neighbouring panel interlocking at Gateshead. At Newcastle Central a panel designed on exactly the same lines as the celebrated one at York was installed in the early 1950s, and this replaced a series of electro-pneumatic interlockings with miniature-lever frames on the north side of the River Tyne. When the Newcastle area was modernized, consequent upon the construction of the King Edward Bridge in 1906, the various junctions on the south side of the Tyne were also equipped with electro-pneumatic interlocking. The majority of these were relatively small and in the course of the present modernization work they too came to be replaced by a panel interlocking. In the period that elapsed between design of the York panel and the construction of the Newcastle one on similar lines, the process of miniaturization, described in earlier chapters of this book, had made possible a very considerable reduction in the overall size of control panels, and at one time it was very seriously considered practicable to build the panel required for Gateshead inside the Newcastle box. Preliminary designs were actually sketched out for accommodating the greatly miniaturized Gateshead panel in the space between the Newcastle Central console and the raised dais. From the viewpoint of traffic regulation it would certainly have been advantageous to have both panels in the same control-room; but other considerations led eventually to the construction of an entirely separate signal-box at Gateshead itself.

CHAPTER XVII

Automatic Driving of Trains

In the years between the two world wars, when there was much divided opinion among railwaymen as to the extent automatic train control should be applied, the practices of overseas countries were carefully studied, and certain fundamental features were accepted as prerequisites of any future British standard system. Perhaps the most important of all principles, so far as the main-line railways were concerned, was that control of the train should not be taken out of the driver's hands except in emergency. Any system should aid and supplement the driver's observance of the wayside signals—not in any way supersede them. All the time a small but highly expert body of opinion advocated systems of continuous rather than intermittent indications in the cab, and the rapid development of the principle of the coded track circuit made the provision of a multiplicity of cab indications a thoroughly practical proposition.

The track circuit in its original and simplest form uses steady-energy current. This current can be d.c., as from a battery, or a.c., from a step-down transformer connected to a mains supply. Some d.c. track circuits are fed from rectifiers. In all these cases the flow of current in the rails is steady all the time. In a coded track circuit the current flows for equal on and off periods. By the use of specially designed coding apparatus the supply can be interrupted so that one has, for example, 120 pulses a minute. That is, the current is on for sixty half-second periods, and off for a corresponding number. By the use of different code-generators, as these instruments are known, codes of 180, 270 or other frequencies per minute can be provided. Working in synchronization with the different codes are 'code following relays', each of which responds only to its particular code. Thus, as an example, a track circuit energized at the 180 code will cause the signal at its entrance to show a single yellow; the 270 code can be arranged to provide the double yellow, and so on. Similarly, inductive pick-up apparatus on the locomotive could be designed to display signals, corresponding to the aspects of the wayside signals, in the engine cab. A trial installation of continuous cab signalling controlled by coded track circuits was made on the former L.N.E.R. main line between New Barnet and Potters Bar, and one of the ex-G.N.R. 'Atlantic' engines equipped with the necessary receiving and indicating apparatus.

It was however not on the main lines but on the London Underground that the most striking developments in the use of coded track circuits for automatic train control came to be made. Ever since the first electrification of the District and Metropolitan lines, and the equipment of the Yerkes tube railways, the closely controlled and uniform pattern of train service operation had facilitated the acceptance of the most inflexible system of automatic train control, namely the train-stop abreast of each stop signal. There was no question of warning or assisting the driver. The action was irrevocable. If a stop signal was over-run by even the slightest margin the train-stop caused a full emergency application of the brakes to be made. This very downright translation of signal indications to control of train movement now has its counterpart in the use of coded track circuits *to drive the train*. The multiplicity of messages that can be provided by the codes applied to the rails in differing circumstances are now used, via the inductive pick-up coils, to drive the train at speeds appropriate to the codes flowing in the rails. This concept, which in other circumstances might be considered revolutionary, or even daring, has now passed well beyond the experimental stage and on September 1, 1968, the first automatically-driven trains began operating in public service on the new Victoria Line tube railway.

Before discussing some of the details of how it has been done it is just as well to pause for a moment to absorb fully the profound significance of what has been achieved in the equipment of the Victoria Line. For this is surely something very near the ultimate in signalling. One is again mindful of the words of the first President of the Institution of Railway Signal Engineers, A. T. Blackall, who I quoted in Chapter I. His prophetic words are even more applicable towards the introduction of the automatic train, and I quote him again:

'Now, if the root idea involved in the expression "signalling" be the control of traffic movements, it is clear that the actual means adopted to effect that control, though essential features, are subsidiary ones. They will vary under varying conditions; they will vary from time to time; they may entail the use of mechanical appliances, of electrical or other power, or they may consist merely in the application of a code of rules. Thus, the primary and most essential function of signalling consists in the consideration, in a comprehensive fashion, of the whole of the conditions which have to be met, and the whole of the requirements which have to be fulfilled; and, having regard to all these, in the working out of a scheme which shall be appropriate from every possible point of view. It is thus obvious that to think of the signalling art as concerned merely, for example, with the installation of semaphores, the connecting up of rail switches, or the equipment of block apparatus, is to take a very incomplete and one-sided view of its functions; it is to think, in fact, of one or more individual parts as representing the whole. Each of the many functions into which a signalling equipment may be divided is important, as assisting to the object which is in view, but it should never be forgotten that the need for any of them may be transient only. By a turn in the wheel of development any one of these may become useless, when to retain it would be merely to hinder progress. Now, it is by cultivating this attitude of mind that the successful signal engineer is produced. He must have at his command all the many schemes and devices and systems and appliances which the experience of many years of development has provided for him; but all these he must regard merely as tools, to be made use of or discarded as the necessities of the moment may demand, in fulfilment of the essential purpose of the art of signalling as I have attempted to define it. Thus, for example—and the conception is not a remote one—if the conditions in a given case could be met most satisfactorily by a signalling system in which there were no semaphores or other visible signals, and no block system, there should be no hesitation in adopting it, and the fact that the ancient features had been scrapped, and the ancient methods discarded, would in no way remove such a scheme from within the definition of a signalling system.'

The signalling of the Victoria Line, following the very important trial installation on the Woodford-Hainault loop, is the latest and most brilliant of all Robert Dell's ingenious contributions to the art of signalling. He has not yet dispensed, as the Pennsylvania Railroad did on certain freight lines in the Pittsburg area, with wayside signals altogether; for the Victoria Line has colour-light signals throughout. But he has virtually dispensed with the driver, for the operator in the cab normally has no other function but to press the starting button, which causes the train doors to close. Technically this could be done equally well by someone on the station platform, and although the automatically-driven train would encounter colour-light signals in its passage from station to station, those signals are nowadays no more than visible indications of the speed controls that would be imposed upon the train through the agency of the coded track circuits and the train-carried apparatus, the operation of which is 'touched off' by the codes picked up inductively. But although one basic function of signalling is the efficient control of traffic movements the prime fundamental is always the safety of passengers, and with this in mind certain elements of the 'belt and braces' order have been embodied in the equipment of the Victoria Line, which it may be found practicable to discard in later extensions of the same system of operation.

To look further into the basic concept, here in the tube tunnels of the Victoria Line is the complete 'loop' of railway traffic control. Railways as they have evolved over more than 150 years have depended on the teamwork of many men for the successful running of even one train, let alone an entire service. Drivers, firemen, signalmen, traffic regulators, permanent-way inspectors and gangers all have a part to play—some continuously, others occasionally—but all in their respective spheres once the guard's whistle is blown to give the driver the right-away. Each can contribute to, or detract from, the punctual running of the train. Over the years it has become well appreciated that the more comprehensive the signalling the better will be the overall regulation of traffic, and the better the running of individual trains; and I need not enlarge at this stage upon the numerous devices that have tried to aid the driver's observance of the wayside signals. 'Interlocking the engine with the signal' was how one form of automatic train control was advertised sixty years ago. Now Robert Dell has brought all these diverse factors into a single scientifically-controlled orbit, set in motion from each station by the pressing of a single button. The one variable factor that now remains is the time the passengers take to entrain or detrain at the stations.

On the Victoria Line the automatic control of the running of the trains consists of two quite distinct 'track-to-train' command systems, and it is most important to appreciate the essential difference between the two. First and foremost the absolute safety of train operation must be ensured, and this is provided by the continuous track-to-train inductive link from the coded track circuits to the pick-up coils on the trains. The four codes that are used, and the effect they have on the train running, are as follows:

Code rate per minute	Command effect on train
120	Emergency brake applied.
180	No motoring allowed under automatic driving conditions. Emergency brake applied if speed exceeds 25 m.p.h.
270	Allows a controlled speed of 22 m.p.h. Permits a restart from a stop between stations. Emergency brake applied if speed exceeds 25 m.p.h.
420	Allows train to run at maximum speed. Permits starting from a station.

The permitted running corresponding to the four codes could be considered as similar to those connected with the familiar indications of four-aspect colour-light signals on main-line railways. Thus the '120' code is equivalent to the 'red', and passing it has the same effect as over-running a stop signal on the older sections of London Transport railways and being tripped by the train-stop. The '180' code is the more extreme degree of caution, as for example the 'single yellow', which on the Victoria Line permits a train to coast at under 25 m.p.h., but does not permit any power to be applied to the traction motors. The '270' code is a lesser degree of caution, still precluding any higher speed than 25 m.p.h., but allowing a train to 'motor' at 22 m.p.h. This code also permits a restart from a signal stop between stations. On the Woodford – Hainault line, where the new system was thoroughly tried out, I have travelled several times in the driver's cab, and it was a fascinating experience to see the automatic restart after a train had been stopped at a 'red' signal, and the signal then cleared. The '420' code is the equivalent of a 'green', indicating full-speed travel.

When continuous inductive automatic train control was first applied in the United States, the apparatus was designed to provide for certain limiting speeds: 'high', 'medium' and 'low', according to the condition of the line ahead, and the speed governing equipment definitely imposed those limits; but all the finer points of speed regulation were in the hands of the driver. On the Victoria Line, following the very successful trials on the Woodford – Hainault loop, all features of the driving and not only the fundamental safety requirements are automatically performed. It is extremely important to ensure a smooth and rapid run-up to a station stop. A prime necessity on all such intensively used lines as the London 'tubes' is to have the facility for very close headway working, and even among the best motormen, on a service worked like the existing ones, there will be differences between the speed of approach to a station made by one driver and another. The 'auto-driver' fitted to the Victoria Line trains provides for completely uniform approaches to afford the closest headway between successive trains.

The overriding safety controls continuously imposed on the train by the coded track circuits are dictated by purely signalling principles according to the state of the line ahead. The brakes would not be applied, for example, unless a train entered into a coded track circuit in which a more restrictive code was flowing. The 'auto-driver' regulates the speed according to the proximity of approach to a station. If the station were already occupied the safety signalling controls derived from the coded track circuits would positively prevent that approach; but if the line was clear the train would have to be controlled by other means. At this stage it is important to appreciate the difference between emergency braking, which would be imposed if a train entered a track circuit in which a restrictive code was flowing, and a normal service application. The latter provides for the maximum rate of deceleration that is considered practicable for ordinary passenger comfort.

London Transport trains are usually very well loaded at the peak periods, with a considerable proportion of the passengers standing. Too rapid a deceleration could cause extreme discomfort, and probably minor injuries.

One needs to apply service, as distinct from emergency braking, not only in the approach to stations, but in running up to a temporary speed restriction due to engineering work, or to an adverse signal, and to provide thus what is termed a 'command system' superimposed upon the fundamental safety controls provided by the coded track circuits. What are termed 'command-spots' are established at the appropriate points along the line. These 'spots' consist of lengths of running rail about ten feet long through which are passed coded currents; but, in contrast to the relatively low frequency of the coded track circuits used in the safety signalling system, the command-spots are fed with current at audio-frequency, approximately 15 and 20 kilo-cycles per *second*. Separate pick-up coils receive these signals, which are duly decoded and fed into the circuitry of the command system on the train.

A single 'command-spot' to provide service braking is provided on the approach side of each signal; but in the approach to a station, running under clear signals, a more accurate control is needed than that possible with a single 20-kc. 'spot'. A series of braking command-spots is provided to check the speed sequentially from the full speed of approach until the train is stopped with precise accuracy at the station platform. The apparatus works with astonishing precision, and on the various occasions when I have travelled on the Woodford – Hainault trains the way in which the train has drawn into a station, and stopped a matter of inches from the point marked on the platform—without any action from the driver—is almost uncanny.

While remaining fascinated by the success of this remarkable technical achievement, the critic may well question what the really practical advantages are from use of such highly sophisticated and inevitably expensive equipment. Such a question was to some extent answered in the concluding paragraphs of a paper read before the Institution of Locomotive Engineers in January, 1967, by the two engineers most directly responsible for the automatic driving and motive power control apparatus on the trains, Messrs W. W. Maxwell and D. K. Ware. They stated that London

Transport expected to obtain the following advantages and benefits from this system of automatic train operation:

(a) Regularity of service due to the consistent driving techniques

(b) Minimizing of energy consumption, by enforcing coasting at a fixed point in the track

(c) The proper observation of speed restrictions

(d) The possibility of making up time and closing up the service by selective elimination of coasting

(f) The opportunity of introducing one-man operation.

The first four of these are highly technical considerations, though the variation in driving practice, even with multiple-unit electric trains, is at times quite remarkable. It goes without saying that a man who consistently makes an ultra-cautious run-in to stations can seriously affect the headway between trains in the entire service. The use of one-man operation is a clear economic advantage, and the possibilities of running trains without any operator at all have already been freely discussed. Technically, the requirements have already been examined, and they do not appear to be insoluble. Without venturing upon the hazardous path of trying to gaze into the future, one would not like to suggest how completely driverless trains could be introduced, in such a form that they could cope with all the rigours and vagaries of rush-hour traffic on the London tube railways.

CHAPTER XVIII

On the Threshold

I end this book at what could prove a very exciting stage in British railway history. I am sure that the automatic operation of trains on the Victoria Line is only the beginning of full automation on rapid-transit urban and suburban lines. On long-distance routes the whole trend is towards substantial acceleration of schedules both for passenger and freight trains on those routes where there is still good business, and where railways can compete with road haulage and equally with internal air services. Thirty-one years ago, in an article contributed to *The Railway Magazine*, I wrote: 'Power signalling to the traffic officer has become one of the most potent instruments for improving train services; more than this—in busy districts, and in electrified areas in particular—it is a dominant factor; without it the present timetables could not be operated.'

This is even more true today. Signalling is the very cornerstone of railway traffic operation, and management turns to the signal engineer for marshalling yard mechanization, for the security in running high-speed train services like those between Euston and Crewe, and for complete automation, as on the Victoria Line. Overseas, where railways are fighting against severe competition, the maximum service speeds of the fastest trains have already passed well beyond the magic 100 m.p.h., in our British system of measures. Our friends on the Continent have already topped the 200 k.p.h. mark, and to make such running safe they have had to introduce special signalling methods. Today the research workers are very active, and there is talk of imminent 'break-throughs' into new, and highly ingenious methods of train control. But looking back over the forty-odd years in which I have been actively

174

engaged in the profession, it is the processes of gradual evolution, the step-by-step advances of men engaged in the day-to-day problems of railway operation, who have produced the most lasting innovations.

One did not progress in one leap from the mechanical locking frame to the relay-interlocked push-button control panel. Earlier chapters of this book have traced the process of evolution, based on hard experience. It was the experience of intensely-locked miniature power frames that led to the introduction of all-electric lever interlocking, and it was a practical railwayman's vision of combining the functions of a signal-box and a 'control' that led to the introduction of panel working. The ever-increasing cost of building construction hastened the miniaturization of signal-box equipment, so that structures could be smaller, and then electronic apparatus began to take the place of traditional signalling equipment.

There is a striking parallel today with the earliest days of railways. The electric locomotive is creating as revolutionary advances in the speed of travel by land as the steam locomotive itself did 140 years ago. Then, from a situation in which man's fastest mode of travel was a galloping horse, we had, in a very few years, trains running at 40 and even 50 m.p.h. At the close of the steam era on British railways very few trains averaged 70 m.p.h. over long distances; today it is only the incidence of occasional speed restrictions to 80 m.p.h. or a little less that prevents London Midland electric trains averaging 100 m.p.h. for hours on end. And both the French and the Germans have trains running at 125 m.p.h.

Twenty miles per hour to forty, seventy to one hundred—the upsurge in speed is comparable, and in both cases one can trace the trend that the development of motive power is drawing just a little ahead of the other adjuncts of safe, high-speed travel. In West Germany and France the ultra-high-speed running is at present confined to one or two specially equipped trains, and the wayside signals have not been changed. To provide adequate braking distance special methods have been introduced to warn drivers of the aspects being displayed by signals far beyond their sight, so that they have advance warning. These measures have their parallel in the operating instructions in force with the L.N.E.R. high-speed streamlined trains in pre-war days between London and York. British practice recently has been towards general acceleration rather than the giving of preferential treatment to a few special trains.

That we are on the threshold of still greater technological advances in railway operating practice cannot be doubted, and I will end by quoting again from that article I wrote in December, 1937. Some of the details rather 'date' that article, but in its broad implications it is still as cogent as it was then:

'At the present time it is no exaggeration to say that the whole field of railway signalling in this country is in process of evolution. One by one the large mechanical interlockings at terminal stations and big junctions are being replaced by power systems; several lengthy sections of main line are now track-circuited throughout and controlled by colour-light signals, while many smaller improvements, such as the shortening of long sections by putting in automatic intermediate block posts, although minor schemes in themselves, are having in the aggregate no small influence on train operation. At the same time every new installation tends to bring forth fresh features. For this the increasingly exacting demands of the traffic departments are to a certain degree responsible, but the latest scientific developments have also played their part. And so, in these islands alone, the power signal installations put into service during the past twenty years show some very striking differences, not only in the apparatus used but also in the root principles on which they are based. Finality to the degree attained with mechanical signalling is not even a vision of the future in the case of power working; in fact, development has become more rapid than ever in the last few years.'

As the concluding chapters of this book have shown, it is even more rapid today.

INDEX